365 Bedtime Stories

OM
Om Books International

First Published in 2007 by

Om Books International
4379/4B Prakash House Ansari Road Darya Ganj
New Delhi 110002. India.
Tel: 91-11-23263363, 23265303
Fax: 91-11-23278091
Email: sales@ombooks.com
Website: www.ombooks.com

Reprint : 2009

ISBN: 978-81-87107-53-8

365
Bedtime Stories

Contents

The Story of the Month: The Remarkable Rocket

January

The Story of the Month

The Remarkable Rocket

01 The Remarkable Rocket

It was a time for celebration in the kingdom of Silver Land. Prince Silver Boy was marrying the very beautiful, Princess Gold. Kings, queens, and noblemen from around the world had gathered in Silver Land to attend their grand wedding. The king ordered his courtiers to arrange a spectacular fireworks display for this special occasion. The preparations began immediately and the best crackers from around the world were collected. But there was one special firecracker—it was the Remarkable Rocket!

The Remarkable Rocket was always saved for the last. It was covered with sparkling gold paper and when set off, it travelled high up into the sky and then burst into a million dazzling stars. People watched the rocket in wonderment. However, the Remarkable Rocket was very proud. The day before the display all the crackers were stocked in the royal garden. The Bright Candle said, "Oh! I am so excited. Imagine, the king of Silver Land ordering a special fireworks display for the wedding. We have to perform well." The Cracker Wheel replied, "Oh, yes we must. Imagine all eyes will be on us!"

"Order, order," interrupted a gruff voice. All the crackers turned and saw the Rocket. "What is there to be so excited?" said Remarkable Rocket. "My forefathers have been part of this display and now it's my turn." "It's a rare honour for us," said Flashy Spinner. "It is no honour for me. The prince is just fortunate to be getting married on the very day that I am being let off," the Rocket snapped back. "Oh dear, what a pompous rocket he is!" thought Bright Candle trying hard to check his laughter. "Why are you laughing?" demanded the rocket. "Oh! I am just very happy for myself," replied Bright Candle. "You should be happy because you have the rare opportunity to be with me!" said the rocket, with his conical head held high. Seeing Remarkable Rocket's unmatchable arrogance, Flashy Spinner tried to explain, "You see, common sense says that you should be happy for others." "Common?! But I am uncommon!" replied the rocket.

"Oh, he can't think beyond himself," whispered Cracker Wheel to the others. "It's no use explaining to him," reasoned Flashy Spinner. Just then they heard the king announcing the finale for the evening, the grand fireworks display!

All the firecrackers, Flashy Spinner, Cracker Wheel, Bright Candle, and several others were placed in rows and then set off. Flashy Spinner showered a golden rain. Cracker Wheel went "BOOM! BOOM!" as she twirled round and round, while Bright Candle shone gently. Finally, it was the turn of the Remarkable Rocket. "I am the best," he thought as he saw innumerable eyes watching him. The king's men set fire to his tail, while everybody waited with bated breath. But lo! Remarkable Rocket did not go off. He was damp and cold. The king's men tried once again but Remarkable Rocket could not be lit. The stocked firecrackers giggled seeing the rocket's poor condition.

The next morning, the king's men came to clear the field. "Oh what a bad rocket it is!" claimed one man. "Did I hear BAD rocket?" thought the vain rocket. "No! It must be GRAND Rocket!" he comforted himself.

Suddenly someone picked it up, crushed it and threw it into a dustbin. "Ouch! That hurts," screeched Remarkable Rocket. "They are committing a mistake by discarding me."

The other crackers in the dustbin, which did not set off that night, were crying, "How unfortunate we are. We could not show our splendour to the king."

"But I am still alive, and will sparkle for the whole world to watch!" said Remarkable Rocket smiling. After a while, the dustbin was picked up and thrown into the river. Remarkable Rocket was nothing but soggy cardboard now and you should have seen his bent head as he drowned. Serves him right for being so arrogant!

02 Charlie Chimp and Louis Lion

Louis Lion had a new wagon and he took it to the playground proudly. "No one can touch it, ride in it, or play with it except for ME!" he said loudly. Charlie Chimp was playing on the seesaw. When he sat on one end, the other end went up, and down he would go with a THUMP! This was no fun at all. Charlie Chimp looked around and spied Louis. "Hey, Louis, come over here and make this balance with me," he shouted cheerily. Louis did and soon the two were enjoying themselves going up and down. Then Louis had an idea. "Charlie, would you like to try out my new wagon?" he asked eagerly. "But Louis, you said no one could play with it," said Charlie looking surprised. "I thought that we could take turns pulling each other in it. It's not much fun alone," admitted Louis. The two of them had learnt it was more fun playing when you share!

03 Teddy's Adventure

While Kumiko was in school, Scraps the dog, playfully tossed Teddy around the house and into a shopping basket. "Ouch!" said Teddy. "There goes my back!" The basket belonged to Kumiko's mother, Mrs. Brown, who was going shopping that day. When she pulled out her purse to pay the bill Teddy fell into a shopping trolley, which rolled down the aisle and bounced Teddy into a garbage can. "Oof!" Teddy exclaimed. Next, a lorry collected the garbage and threw it in the dump. "Cheep, Cheep!" a bird picked teddy up. Teddy was too heavy for her and she dropped him while flying over a school. Miss Angus found Teddy and put him on a shelf along with the other toys. Teddy was feeling sorry for himself when he heard a familiar voice. "How did you come to school, Teddy?" asked Kumiko. "It's a long, long story," thought Teddy.

04 The Boy in the Paper Boat

Jack loved making paper boats. One day he made a paper boat and kept it on his bedside table. A loud noise woke him up at night. To his astonishment Jack saw a captain and three sailors getting ready to set sail in his paper boat!

"Where are you going?" asked Jack sleepily. "Why don't you come aboard, Mate?" replied the captain and that's exactly what Jack did. "Yipee!" he shouted as the paper boat set off across the sea, which filled his room, out of his house and down the street towards the shopping mall. In the parking lot, they met a fearsome-looking ship filled with pirates. "Let's give them a good fight, my boy," shouted the captain. "Aye, aye captain," replied Jack with glee. Jack fought like a hero and very soon the pirate ship sank. Afterwards, the paper boat dropped Jack off on his bed and it always remains on his bedside table in case the captain needs his help!

05 The Lucky Seed

A farmer was on his way to the market to sell a bag of seeds. His cart bumped into a stone and a seed fell out of the bag. "I wish I could be safe underground," thought the seed. A passing buffalo pushed the seed into the ground! "I am so thirsty. I need some water to help me grow," thought the seed. It began to rain! The next day the seed had a green shoot. The sun came out and the shoot grew taller. Then a leaf appeared. A hungry bird tried to pluck and eat the seed but the roots saved it. Many years passed and the seed grew into a plant and then into a fine, strong tree. Now don't you think that the seed was lucky?

06 The Teacher's Secret

There was a teacher who liked to snack while he taught. He told the children that the snack was only for grown-ups and was poisonous for children. One day while the teacher was away, a child said, "Why don't we take a look at the teacher's snack?" The children peeped into the basket and instead of some awful medicine as they had imagined the children saw berries.

The children ate up all the berries! They were delicious. "What shall we do now?" cried one of them in a panic, "we will be punished." So what do you think they did? The children upset the teacher's table and inkstand and then lay down on the floor. They told the teacher they had toppled his table by mistake and to pay for their mistake they had eaten the poisonous berries so that they would die. The teacher, of course, knew better!

07 The Adventures of Molly and Ho Ho

Every year, Molly and her kitten Ho Ho helped her father sell balloons at the fair. Molly had learnt how to fill the balloons with air and tie them up with a string. "I wish we could go to the fair," said Molly to Ho Ho who meowed in agreement. Suddenly Molly had an idea. "Usually Daddy has a whole lot of balloons in the garage and mother has a clothes basket. Come on, let's go find a ball of string," she said and the two of them ran to the garage. Molly placed the clothes basket in her wagon and filled it with rock. Then she tied several balloons to the sides of the basket as she had once seen on a TV show. The basket started moving. "Time to get in before it flies away," said Molly and they pulled the basket outside and hopped into it. Molly threw the rocks out and slowly the basket rose into the air. Molly's mother saw them and shouted to them to stop but it was too late. The balloon sailed over the treetops until finally Molly saw the fair grounds below them. She cut the balloons free and the basket slowly landed. Molly was surprised to see a policeman, her parents, and a whole crowd of people waiting for her. "Don't ever do that again!" scolded her parents. Molly realised her mistake and said she was sorry. "Meow," added Ho Ho.

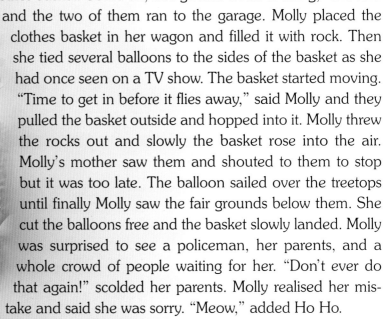

08 Rodney Rhino's Weekend Plans

Rodney Rhino was looking forward to the weekend. He could do what he loved best—play with his friends. Rodney called up Sammy Snake. "Let's take our bikes and go for a ride," he said. "SSSorry, Rodney. I have got football practice today, a game tomorrow, and on SSSSunday I have to go for a birthday party," said Sammy. Disappointed, Rodney called up Gilbert Gator. "Let's build something with my blocks," he said. But Gilbert Gator was busy too. His father was taking him fishing. Rodney was fed up. He went outside and lay down on the grass staring grumpily at the clouds. Everyone had something to do. He heard a voice calling to him and looked up to see his mother. His friend Louis Lion had called. He wanted to play football with him the next day. "It's going to be a good weekend after all," smiled Rodney.

09 Sunny Day's Favourite Sounds

Sunny Day admired the sound of a brook as he flowed over the pebbles. "You make such a wonderful sound, Babbling Brook," he said. "Thank you, Sunny Day," replied Babbling Brook continuing on his way.

Sunny Day heard a bee buzzing as it collected honey. "How do you make that sound?" he asked. "I have to flex my muscles and rub my wings to keep my body warm while I work," replied the bee. "That's what makes that buzzing sound."

Sunny Day heard Mocking Bird singing a song. "That's a lovely sound," he said. "How do you do it?" "I don't know," replied Mocking Bird. "When I have a happy thought I open my mouth and sing."

Sunny Day heard children laughing. "I love that sound," he said to one little boy. "How do you do it?" "When I find something funny I laugh. It feels good," replied the little boy. Sunny Day thought how lucky he was to hear so many wonderful sounds.

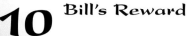

10 Bill's Reward

Bill was walking back from school one day when he found a black-and-white dog caught in a trap behind a bush. He took the dog home to his parents. "I think it has a broken leg," said Bill's father. "Let's take her to the vet." The vet put a cast on the dog's leg and also told them that she was going to have puppies. Bill was very excited. "Wow!" he said "I wish she was mine. I must find her owners quickly." He put up signs around the neighbourhood with a description of the dog and his phone number. A few days later, the owner phoned and then came to collect his dog. He praised Bill for taking such good care of his dog. "You are such a good boy that once the puppies are born you may have one for yourself," said the owner. "Oh, thank you," cried Bill overjoyed.

11 The Monkey and the Caps

Once upon a time a young boy used to sell caps. One afternoon, while he was taking a nap under the shade of a tree a group of monkeys came and took all his caps away. When the boy awoke he was shocked to see that the monkeys were swinging from the trees, wearing his colourful caps. "Give back my caps!" he shouted angrily. But the monkeys were too busy eating bananas. So he thought of a plan. He clapped his hands and jiggled his waist. Since monkeys love to mimic others, they too started clapping and jiggling their waists. The boy then took off his cap and threw it on the ground. The foolish monkeys copied his action and threw their caps on the ground. The boy quickly collected his caps and left that place.

8

12 A Duck's Tale

Huang ran a poultry farm. There were ducks of all hues and sizes in his farm—white ducks, brown ducks, ducks with stripes, and ducks with specks. Every morning, Huang and his two workers, Bill and Jim, would go around the city in a big truck. They supplied ducks and eggs to schools, restaurants, and canteens. One day, Huang set off on his round. At his first stop Huang counted, "One, two, three, four—four ducks for St Peter's," and carried them into the school kitchen. Tom, a naughty boy thought, "Now for some fun." He opened the truck door and one by one all the ducks came down. "Quack! Quack!!" they went all the way into the school. Soon the whole school was filled with quacking ducks. Children came out of their classrooms and screamed in joy. Hearing the commotion, Huang came out. "Come back!" he said and made a quacking sound and all the ducks came back to him.

13 The Little Rose Plant

A little Rose plant lived inside a dark damp room. One day she heard a soft tapping on her door, "Who's there?" she asked. "I am little Raindrop. Please let me in," cried the visitor. "No way!" said the Rose plant angrily. Little Raindrop was very sad for being turned away. After sometime the Rose plant heard a soft rustle near the door. "Who's there now?" she asked. "I am Sunny Sunshine," said the new visitor. "I don't have time for sunshine," said the Rose plant haughtily. A few days later, the leaves of the Rose plant turned brown in colour, and her young stem began drooping. Then one day, she heard the chirping of birds, and opened her door to see outside. It was spring and there were colourful flowers and greenery all around. The Rose plant realised her mistake. So when Rain and Sunshine returned, she welcomed them warmly. And after a few days she had a pretty pink rose, for which she thanked the Raindrop and the Sunshine.

14 The Price of Pride

An oyster lived inside his shell on the ocean bed. He thought himself to be the most important creature in the world because he could make pearls! One day, a huge wave tossed him to the seashore. The oyster disliked the seashore and yearned to return home. Just then a crow spotted the beautiful oyster and pecked his shell, "Who's there?" asked the oyster. "I am a crow and I want to see what you look like," said the crow. "Get lost you ugly creature," snapped the oyster, "I am the oyster which makes pearls for the rich and the beautiful. Why should I open my doors for you?" The crow was offended. Grabbing the shell in his beak, he flew high up into the sky. Then he opened his mouth and dropped it. The shell broke into several fragments and the pearl rolled into a pool of muddy water. The oyster watched helplessly as the crow flew away cawing merrily.

15 Lonely Emma's Wallpaper

Emma had no siblings or any friends. Every night, before going to bed Emma would gaze at the white wooly sheep on the wallpaper in her room and count them one by one. One day, Emma's mother changed the wallpaper in her room. It was jungle wallpaper and had pictures of all the animals. Emma was very happy that night and before going to bed started counting the animals. Suddenly she heard a soft whine. She opened the window and found a little baby bear crying. "Why are you crying, Baby Bear?" she asked. "I don't remember the way to the jungle where my parents live," answered the bear. "You can spend the night here and help me count the animals on my jungle wallpaper." The bear joined Emma and together they counted all the animals. Next morning, before leaving for home the bear said, "I'll tell all the animals about your wallpaper!" From that day onwards, Emma had new visitors every day and she was never lonely again.

16 The Little Engine

A little steam engine was given the task of pulling a train of cars. His wheels chugged along the iron tracks and puffed clouds of steam. After some time, the engine halted before a huge hill. "Oh now I have to climb this steep hill," gasped the tired engine. He gathered his strength, blew the whistle, and rolled his wheels. But he failed to pull the train of cars. He looked around him and saw another steam engine standing next to him, "Please help me pull the train over the hill," he said. "Don't you see I have wagons full of coal to pull?" snapped the other engine. Suddenly he spotted a big engine rolling into the sidetracks. Surprisingly it did not go past him, but halted next to him. "What happened?" enquired the engine. When the little engine explained his problem, the new engine went and stood behind the train. Together they sang, "We can, we shall," and slowly went up the hill. The little engine thanked the new engine and went home whistling merrily.

17 The Big Wooden Toy Box

Tom and Rosie had a big wooden toy box. The box had a huge collection of dolls, teddy bears, skipping ropes and dinky cars. Tom and Rosie's room always looked tidy because the toys were all packed in the big wooden box. However, the toys were very unhappy with this. "We are all stuffed in the dark," said a dinky car. "I can't even stretch my legs," lamented the rag doll. "And my rope is always tangled," grieved the skipping rope. "Let's try and push the lid and get out of here," suggested the teddy bear. They tried hard but could not open the lid. One day, Tom and Rosie's father was busy sorting out his tools in the garage. "Could we help you, Father?" asked Tom. "Sure. You can tidy up my tool boxes," said their father. Now Father's tools were all lying scattered. He had some small boxes but needed a big box. "Could we exchange your big toy box with these boxes?" suggested father. "That's a great idea," said Tom excitedly. They collected all the boxes and ran into their room. Each toy was placed in a separate box. Tom and Rosie were happy as they could still keep the room tidy and as for the toys, they never had to live in the dark again.

18 Mulligan the Police Dog

Mulligan was a fiery police dog. Thieves, robbers and bandits shook in their boots when they saw Mulligan patrolling the streets of Huskerville. He showed his teeth and growled at them. Now, the butterflies had a special liking for Mulligan. They loved him and Mulligan loved them too. Wherever Mulligan went, the butterflies followed him. Huskerville was filled with butterflies. The citizens complained to the police, "There are too many butterflies in this town. We have to get rid of Mulligan." So Mulligan was removed from service. But as soon as he left, the thieves and robbers became nastier. They robbed people, scared them and kidnapped little kids. People were worried and an emergency meeting was called. "Bring back Mulligan," demanded one man. "We can bear those butterflies but have to get rid of the criminals," said another man. Soon Mulligan rejoined service and the criminals fled Huskerville. However, the butterflies were back again, but this time they had many more admirers.

19 The Seat of Honour

During the annual feast held in the jungle, the seat of honour was reserved for the eldest animal. However, this year a severe argument began as to who was the oldest. The deer said, "I am the eldest for I created the sun and the moon." The fox interrupted, "But I made the ladder which you used to climb up to the sky. So I am the eldest here." Now an old toad asked, "Are you talking about the ladder which was used to create the sun and moon?" "Yes, yes," said the fox excitedly. "I remember my great grandchild, who is no more," said the toad wiping his tears, "telling me that he had planted the tree which was used to make the ladder." Hearing the toad's story, no other animal complained and the seat of honour was given to him.

20 Two Bad Mice

Tom Thumb and his wife Hunca Munka were two bad mice. They lived in a small corner of a big house. They nibbled away food in the kitchen and littered it. One night, they saw something unique. It was a doll's house and had little tables, chairs, beds, and also a table with food. The two tiptoed into the house and discovered that it was a lot of fun. "The bed fits our size," said Hunca Munka. "But we must finish the food first," explained Tom anxiously. But lo! When they bit the ham, it hurt. They tried the bread too but Tom's tooth almost broke. "This is not real!" sighed Tom. The two bad mice were very disappointed. But while going back to their hole they carried the little beds and chairs along with them. "At least something will be of use," said Hunca Munka.

21 At the Seaside

Ryan and his friends went on their bikes to the seaside. What a thrilling time they had! There were so many people on the beach. There were ice-creams, popcorn and candies all over. Ryan and his friends had everything. Ryan and Boris loved the popcorn while Kate had large scoops of ice-creams. "Look there!" said Kate pointing at two clowns who were doing a funny jig. They also showed their tricks with different colourful balls and played many games with the children. But what the children loved most were their pony rides. After this Ryan, Boris and Maria went to a quieter side of the beach and made a big sand castle. "When we'll grow up we'll stay together in a b-i-g castle like this beside the sea. Won't we?" said Maria jubilantly. "Yes we will," said the boys excitedly. Soon it was time to go back and the children returned home after a fun-filled day.

22 The Lonely Traffic Light

Tiffany the traffic light stood at a crossing, blinking red, green and yellow. She was very sad and lonely. "Nobody cares for me!" she sighed. "All they do is drive by so fast!" But Tiffany felt happy when the light was red and the cars had to wait for her to turn green. "Now everyone is looking at me!" she thought happily. Tiffany loved children who looked out of the car and watched her till she turned green. On some days, they would wave at Tiffany too. One day, poor Tiffany could not change colours. Honk! Honk! All the cars were stuck. Two repairmen who came to fix Tiffany were talking to each other, "We need to repair this light very soon! Just look at the traffic jam!" Now, Tiffany realised how important she was to the cars on the street. "From today onwards, I will work well and keep everyone happy!"

23 Angels in Heaven

Did you know that angels in heaven danced when you were born? Some angels played the piano, some blew the trumpet, while some others clashed the cymbals! Everyone was happy that you were born! The oldest angel, Agnelius had a long, flowing white beard. He stroked it smooth and asked the younger angels, "Hmm… what do you think this baby will grow up to be?" One angel said, "Sire! This baby will become an artist or a dancer!" Another one said, "No, Sire! The baby will become a surgeon!" A third angel said, "This baby will become a teacher or a lawyer!" "Hmm… so many choices for our sweet little baby, eh?" laughed old Agnelius. The youngest angel then spoke up, "Sire, I am scared for this baby!" "Why?" asked Agnelius. "Well…" sighed Youngestus, "What if this cute baby is too short or too tall? What if he lisps while he talks or limps while he walks? What if he becomes deaf or wears glasses or braces? What if the other children make fun of the way he talks or dresses?" Old Angelius laughed, "Ha! Ha! You see, it's OK. He is perfect no matter what others may say!" And all the other angels agreed and said, "We will smile on him forever while he grows. We adore this baby exactly this way!"

24 The Rainbow

There were seven naughty children in the court of Indra, the king of gods. One day, the children had an argument about who is the greatest among them. Red said, "I am the greatest! Watermelons, pomegranates, and apples are red!" "But oranges, carrots, and grains are orange!" cried Orange. "No! I am the best! Sunflowers and bananas are yellow!" said Yellow. Now Green spoke, looking wise, "All unripe fruits are green! Thus, I am the greatest!" "Look at the sky and you will know that I am the best!" declared Blue scornfully. "Haven't you seen peacocks?" asked Indigo. "You surely haven't seen lovely grapes!" cried Violet. When Indra heard this, he said, "Good children never fight! If you play together and be united, you will be even greater than you already are!" The children went off to play in the sky, together. Even today, when they play everybody exclaims at their magical beauty. After all, together they form the rainbow!

25 Snakeman

Bob was fond of snakes. All day long, he would read about snakes and watch TV shows about them. The other children thought Bob was weird and called him "Snakeman." One day, Miss Beetle, their teacher said, "Class, I want you all to write ten lines about butterflies!" Now, Bob did not know anything about butterflies because all he ever read about was snakes. When everybody else gave in their papers, poor Bob had not written a single word. Miss Beetle was angry and was about to punish him. Just then, Mary-Jane ran into the class crying, "Miss Beetle! There is a snake in the lawn." Hearing this, Miss Beetle fainted. Someone called the firemen. But even the firemen were scared of the huge snake! Bob went out to the lawn and quickly grabbed the snake and threw it far away! Bob was not scared of the snake because he knew so much about them! Now, everybody loved Bob.

26 The Snowman

Brrr! It was a cold day. Katie and Melwin wore their jackets and caps and went out to play in the garden. "Look!" cried Melwin. The snow had turned their lawn milky white! "Let's make a snowman!" said Katie. They rolled two balls of snow and placed one on top of the other. They used sticks for making his hands. It was such fun!

On Christmas eve, when Katie and Melwin looked at their snowman, he waved back at them. "The snowman is alive!" both cried in unison. "Shall I give you a Christmas gift?" the snowman asked. He waved his arms and lo! Silver flakes fell from the sky! It was snowing! The children jumped with joy. They gave him a carrot for his nose, a scarf for his neck and a cap for his head.

When the sun came out, the snowman began to melt. "Bye-bye children! Please make me again next Christmas!" he said while Katie and Melwin waved him goodbye.

27 Fabian's Bicycle

Every time Fabian sleeps, he dreams of a fuzzy bicycle. It has an orange seat and silver tassels. The shining bell on the handle goes "Trrring." There are orange clouds beneath the pedals. So, if Fabian falls, he never gets hurt. There are always a dozen birds flying in front of Fabian's bicycle and together they have many an adventure. He meets fairies and pixies and millions of stars in the sky. Once he even gave Santa a ride! Santa gave him a huge bag of goodies as a present too! Everybody loved his orange bicycle. Sadly, Fabian can never ride his fuzzy bicycle when he is awake. But he doesn't mind. He always remembers his nighttime journeys. The fuzzy bicycle remains a secret that no one, except Fabian, knows. He loves bedtime when he and his fuzzy bicycle can set off for their adventures again!

28 What Will I Be When I Grow up?

It was Timmy's birthday and Miss Bessy asked Timmy, "What will you become when you grow up?"

Timmy said, "I can be like my brother. He is a vet who takes care of lizards and snakes! Or I can be like my father. He is a scientist who works to save rare birds and animals."

"Or else," Timmy said, "I can be like my mother who is a dog groomer. Or I could become like my sister. She is a dolphin trainer who loves swimming!"

Timmy sighed and continued, "Miss Bessy, I really love animals but I still can't decide how I will be helpful to them when I grow up."

"Never mind, Timmy. You have a long time to think. After all, you turned just seven years today!" smiled Miss Bessy.

29 Harold and the Purple Crayon

One Day, Harold went out to the park with his brand new purple crayon. "I am going to draw pictures on the park bench," thought naughty Harold.

Getting there, Harold drew a fearsome dog on a park bench. To his surprise, the dog became alive and ran about chasing Mrs. Miles' cat, Peggy! "My purple crayon is magical!" cried Harold. Naughty Harold then drew a long snake that too came alive. The snake slithered through the grass and scared little Timmy who was playing nearby. "Ha! Ha!" Harold laughed hard holding his tummy.

"Now, let me draw a policeman," thought Harold. As he finished drawing, the policeman, in his shiny blue uniform, became alive. "You there!" the policeman yelled. "Don't you know it's wrong to draw on park benches? Come with me to the police station!" Harold was very scared and he begged the policeman to let him go. Harold then ran away, promising never ever to draw on park benches again.

30 Why the Sea Is Salty?

Haiku was a poor man. One day, he went to his rich brother for help. "I have no money to spare you," said his brother. Haiku walked back sadly. He saw a shiny pebble on the road and picked it up absentmindedly. Suddenly he heard a voice say, "This pebble will grant you three wishes." Haiku was overjoyed at his luck. Overnight, he became rich and lived happily. When his brother heard about his change of fortune he stole the pebble. To escape from Haiku, he jumped on a boat and rowed out to the sea. He prayed to the pebble to give him salt, which he could sell for a rich sum. The pebble churned heaps of salt. Unfortunately not knowing how to stop the churning, the boat became full of salt. It overturned and drowned the wicked brother. As for the pebble, it is still churning salt from the bottom of the sea!

31 When the Clock Fell Sick

Once in a tiny town, there was a huge clock that sat on top of a bank building. Everything was going on fine, until one fine day, the clock fell ill.

The clock would skip a minute or two on some days. But on other days, it would run perfectly fine, Tick tock! Tick tock! Gradually, the clock's health began to worsen. Sometimes, it ran two hours too early, on other days it ran two hours too late.

One day, a little child burst into tears because he thought he was late for a birthday party. He rushed to where the party was, and found out that he was there on time, indeed!

Then another day, an army major drove past the clock and adjusted his watch according to it. Now, his watch was running three hours too early. Early next morning, the major ordered his men to begin their six-o'clock ten-mile jog at three in the morning! Now, the men were not very happy about this and they all marched to the bank, together.

The bank manager was a kind lady. She agreed to take the sick clock to a 'clocktor', or if it got worse, to the clock hospital! She met a skilled clocktor who gave her the replacement parts of the clock. Together, they all fixed the poor town clock and set it up on the bank building once again.

Now, the whole town was happy. After all, they could all reset their watches and were dot on time, every day!

Contents

The Story of the Month

Mitty's New Friend

01 Mitty's New Friend

Mitty the kitten lived in a big house. She had many friends—Bob the bumblebee, Betty the butterfly and Bitsy, the little sparrow. Mitty loved her friends. She played with them, shared her food and on cold nights let them stay in her house.

One day, while Mitty was lolling in her garden she heard a soft purr. She peeped round the corner of her house. To her surprise she found a plump little kitten, just like her. "Hello. My name is Gidget and I am your new neighbour," said the kitten. "Yippee!" cried an excited Mitty. She clapped her hands, swished her tail and hopped around in glee. "That's not becoming of a lady like you," said Gidget sternly. "Watch me," she purred, walking daintily. "You are clever! What else can you teach me?" asked Mitty. "Oh, I can teach you numbers and all about colours," replied Gidget. Just then came Bitsy tweeting. "Let's go and play, Mitty," said she. "Meet my new friend Gidget," said Mitty. "This ugly sparrow is your friend?" asked Gidget. Mitty was surprised to hear Gidget talk like that. Bitsy was hurt and she went away.

After some time Bob and Betty came fluttering their wings. "Hey Mitty, let's have lunch." "Hi! Betty, Bob, meet Gidget, my new friend," said Mitty. "Hi Gidget," said Betty warmly. But Gidget did not reply, instead she looked at Mitty and asked, "Will you share your lunch with this big old butterfly?" Mitty was shocked. "Now that's enough," she protested. "You will not speak to my friends like that," said Mitty and walked away in search of her friends.

Bob, Bitsy and Betty called an urgent meeting. "It seems Mitty has forgotten us in favour of her new friend," they lamented. Soon Mitty arrived. "I am sorry, my friends," apologised Mitty. "Your new friend is very rude," protested Bitsy. "She called me old and big," complained Betty. "Betty you're the most beautiful butterfly in the world and Bitsy, you're not ugly," exclaimed Mitty. She added, "Gidget is very rude, I will not talk to her anymore." Mitty wiped her friends' tears and all were happy to be together again.

After some time Gidget arrived. Everyone looked at Gidget cautiously. "Friends, I am sorry," said Gidget. "We don't need a rude friend like you," said Mitty. "Oh Mitty! I thought I was so clever till I came here and found that knowing about colours, numbers and etiquette is not enough. One has to have a good heart and be a good friend," explained Gidget. Mitty and her friends watched wide-eyed while Gidget continued, "Oh Mitty you might not know many things but you are a good kitten. Looking at you and your friends I have learnt so much. Please accept my apology." Mitty and her friends looked at each other. They knew Gidget was not lying. "Okay, we accept your apology, but there's one condition," said Mitty sternly. Everyone held their breath. "You have to teach us all about colours and numbers," said Mitty smiling. All the animals laughed aloud. Gidget became a good friend and a great neighbour.

02 Barbolito's Bad Day at School

Barbolito was a little boy. He was short and had curly hair. The other boys in his class always jeered at him. One day his mother saw him crying, "What is the matter, Barbolito?" she asked. "All the boys make fun of me because I look different," explained Barbolito. "They are foolish boys," explained his mother, "Children often say hateful things to each other because it makes them feel important to look down on someone. I will speak to your teacher." The next day when Barbolito went to school his teacher called him aside and said, "You should not cry because people say mean things. Why don't you talk about all the exciting things you do, like scuba diving and chess. This way the children will get to know you better and will also discover how special you are." That day, Barbolito spoke about his wonderful experiences under sea. He had many curious listeners and made many friends too.

03 Cliff the Adventurer

Cliff loved adventure sports. One day while rock climbing, it began to rain heavily. He took out the survival manual from his bag and read the instructions, "If you see a whale, jump on it." Cliff looked into the deep blue ocean. Suddenly he heard a shrill call. "It's a whale!" Cliff said excitedly. As soon as it neared the edge of the mountain, Cliff jumped and fell right on the whale's back. The whale carried Cliff to the seashore. When Cliff reached the shore he found many people running hither and thither. "Are you a climber?" asked a boy. "Please save us from the flood. People are being swept away." Cliff sat on the whale's back and rescued all the people one by one. He carried them safely back to the mountain. "Cliff, you are a not only a great climber, but also a great boy," said everyone and thanked Cliff for saving their lives.

04 Little Nick

Nick the deer lost his way in the woods. He had been wandering with the rest of the deer but had managed to stray away from them. He was lonely and miserable. One day, while looking for his family he found himself in a farmer's field. He made his way to the people standing in the yard. The farmer's dog barked at Nick at first, but Nick was such a friendly little deer that he soon made friends. Everyone welcomed Nick. The farmer's children loved his soft brown eyes and spotted skin. The farmer let him stay with his cows. Soon Nick and the other animals became good friends. Nick was happy but he still missed his family. One day, while playing, Nick looked out into the fields and saw a herd of deer. "That looks like my family," he said with great hope. Indeed, it was his family. Nick thanked all the animals in the field and said goodbye to them. Everyone was sad to see Nick leave but they knew that they could not keep him away from his family.

05 The Man Who Saved the Moon

One night, a foolish man was crossing the forest. He had been walking for some time and felt tired and thirsty. When he came upon a well he thought he would quench his thirst. He bent down to pull the water out. He saw the reflection of the moon in the well and sighed, "The moon has fallen into the well. I must save it." He quickly fetched a rope and a hook to pull up the moon. He tied the hook to the rope and then dropped it into the well. Suddenly, the hook hit a heavy stone. "Aha, I've got the moon," thought the foolish man. The man pulled hard. He pulled and pulled and pulled. But the stone would not budge. Suddenly, the stone moved and the force made the man fall flat on his back. He lay there unconscious for a while and when he regained his senses, the first thing he saw was the moon was in the sky. He said, "Thank God I saved the moon."

06 The King and His Hawk

Once upon a time a king was crossing the sultry desert. His pet hawk was perched on his shoulders as usual. The hot sun made him thirsty and he went to look for a stream. Luckily, he chanced upon a fountain not very far. He knelt down and was about to drink the water, when suddenly the hawk swooped down and pecked his hand. The king was very surprised at this odd behavior of his pet. He stooped down to drink the water again. But the hawk pecked his hand again. In a fit of rage, the thirsty king drew his sword and killed the hawk. When he stooped down, something glistened in the water. It was a fierce poisonous snake. The king knew that a single sip of that water would have killed him. He now understood what the hawk had been trying to do. He sat beside the dead hawk and moaned, "I have lost you because of my impatience. All you were trying to do was to save my life!"

07 Nine of Ten

A man was crossing the hot desert with his herd of camel. He mounted one and counted the herd, "One, two…nine. I had ten camels, how come there are only nine now?" he wondered. He dismounted and searched frantically for the tenth camel. When he returned to the herd he once again counted the animals. Lo! He found that there were ten of them. After walking a while he felt tired and climbed one camel. To be sure that none of the camels had wandered away, he counted them, "Nine camels again!" The man was utterly confused and did not understand why one animal was missing again. "Oh! These disobedient camels are playing hide and seek with me on a hot summer day!" he said angrily and got off the camel. Finally the foolish man concluded, "I would rather walk and have ten camels around me than ride one and have nine only!"

08 The Cold Planet

Thousands of miles from Earth is the planet of Fliptune. Fliptune gets no sun, and is therefore always cold and dark. It is inhabited by creatures who resemble dinosaurs. These creatures use torches to see. One day, a young Fliptunese called Neila put the wrong batteries in his torch. Suddenly the torch lit up and its bright golden rays travelled through the universe and touched planet Earth. The light hit a boy named Bamby. Even before Bamby could understand what was happening, he got sucked into the light and went higher and higher and landed on Fliptune. Neila watched wild-eyed. He had never seen a human before. Bamby was equally surprised. "It's so cold and dark here," said Bamby. "We don't get the sun," lamented Neila "I can get the sun for you," replied Bamby. He lit the torch once again and helped Bamby return to Earth. Bamby took out a huge mirror and reflected the sun's rays towards Fliptune. Now Fliptune was never dark and cold again.

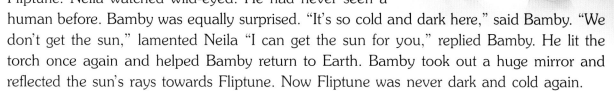

09 The Chinese New Year

Fee-Ying Liu is a little Chinese girl. On every New Year's Eve, Fee opens wide the doors and windows of her house as Mama said the old year could then easily leave the house. Fee loves the Chinese New Year. On this day, she wears new clothes and goes out with her parents to watch the colourful parades that snake through her town. Fee's favourite is to watch people dress up as dragons and perform the dragon dance, while others marched along the streets with lanterns in their hand. All homes are decorated with lights, colourful confetti, flowers, and bamboo plants. Fee enjoys helping Mama put up the colourful festoons. Sometimes even Daddy helps. Like always, this year too Fee will have many friends and relatives visiting her home. Mama has prepared sweets and special dishes for them. But Fee is most excited about the red envelope that her parents will gift her at night. It's a lucky charm and will contain money for Fee to buy new dolls.

10 The Barren Tree

David had a huge apple orchard, which bore the finest apples. One day, a neighbour asked David to lend him a tree. David was a kindhearted man. He graciously gave his neighbour a tree and told him to take precious care. The neighbour went home happily. But now he was in a fix. He wondered where he should place the apple tree. He did not want to place the tree in his garden, for he was scared that passersby might rob the delicious fruits. He did not want to plant it near the door either for his children might pick them. After thinking hard he planted the tree behind his house where the sun hardly ever visited. A whole year went by but the tree did not bear any fruit. Slowly the branches drooped and died. The neighbour angrily accused David of giving him a barren tree. David listened carefully to what had happened and then replied, "How do you expect a rich and generous harvest with a greedy and mean heart?"

11 The Magic Spell

Bill and Crosby were two naughty boys who were always up to some mischief. One evening, they got together to create a magic spell. Bill added his dirty socks and six dead lizards, while Crosby poured a magic potion into the boiling water in the cauldron. Suddenly a huge cloud of smoke bellowed towards Bill's face and lo! his nose was replaced by an elephant's trunk. "Yikes!" screamed Bill in horror. He rushed into his room and searched the Internet for help. One web site read www.helpformagicspells.com. Bill clicked on the link and read the instructions, "To undo a bad spell, you have to be a good boy. Be nice to everyone and never make mischief." Bill and Crosby swore never to be naughty again and quietly went to bed. The next morning Bill was scared to get up from bed. Slowly he raised his head from the covers and looked at the mirror. Hurrah! The elephant's trunk was gone and he had got back his nose.

12 Fool's Luck

One day, a foolish man went to town to sell their ox. He did not tell his elder brothers who were cleverer than him of his plans. On the way, a sudden storm arose. The foolish man heard the trees creaking and thought that they were speaking to him. He asked the willow tree, "I think you wish to buy my ox." The tree creaked even louder and the fool thought that the tree had agreed to buy his ox. He tied the ox to the tree. He told the tree that he would come to fetch the money later. When he reached home and told his brothers about the deal, they laughed and ridiculed him for his stupidity. The foolish man went back to the tree in anger. He cut down the tree in rage when it didn't give him the money. Lo and behold! He found a pot of gold coins under the fallen tree trunk. The foolish man now became a rich man but he always remained kind to his brothers.

13 Why the Chimes Rang

In a faraway land there was a very old church. On top of the church tower there hung beautiful chimes. Every Christmas night, the chimes would start ringing by themselves.

Do you know why?

The people of the land believe that long before the church was built, a young man and his wife once had taken shelter on Christmas night under a tree behind the church. That night the wife gave birth to a baby boy. Suddenly, there appeared a very bright star in the sky only to disappear soon. Before leaving, the next morning the young couple placed a few bells under the tree as a token of their respect to God. Years later, when the church was being built, the bells were found by a mason. He hung them on the tower. Since then they have rung on every Christmas.

14 The Little Red Hen

On a farm there lived many animals and birds. One day, little Red Hen found a grain of wheat in the farmyard.

She asked the other birds, "Who wants to plant this wheat?"

The duck and the goose were lazy and quickly refused to do any work.

So, the little Red Hen planted the grain of wheat. When the wheat was ripe, the little Red Hen again asked the other birds, "Who will take the wheat to the mill?" The duck and the goose again ignored the little Red Hen and continued playing. When it was time to make bread with the flour, the little Red Hen did the work all by herself. At last it was time to eat the bread. The duck and the goose stood close thinking that they too would get a share. But the Red Hen said, "I will eat the bread alone because only I worked for it." She called her chicks and they all had a feast.

15 Circus Escape

Billy was excited! He was watching a circus for the first time. "Oooh!" his eyes widened as the majestic lions entered the ring. "Look, Billy," said Mom pointing to the clowns. Everyone laughed at their funny acts and silly jokes. Billy laughed so hard that he nearly fell off his chair.

Suddenly, there was a loud trumpeting noise and out came three swaying elephants. "There's a baby one too!" squealed Billy in delight. "What is he doing?"

To the amazement of all, the small elephant ran out of the ring and down the stage and out of the circus tent. "Minny! Come back," shouted the elephant trainer.

But Minny was too excited. She ran into the supermarket causing panic among the shoppers. She helped herself to a heap of buns and bananas. She reached a lake and filled water in her trunk and sprayed it on all the passersby. After a good day out, Minny was back in the circus and happy to be with her friends again.

16 Let's Go on a Picnic

On a pleasant spring day, the animals in the woods decided to go for a picnic.

"It's a perfect day for a picnic," said the fox delightedly. Soon the animals gathered with their food and the picnic basket was full. All the friends set off towards the meadow. On the way they came across a stream. "Let's climb that log that has fallen across the stream," suggested the fox. The animals were pleased with the idea and quickly the fox, the rabbits and the porcupine wobbled their way over the log. When the animals reached the meadow, they found the chipmunks had already reached with the basket and had laid out the picnic. "How come you two are here so early?" enquired the fox. The chipmunks grinned and said, "We noticed that the log was hollow so we scampered through it along with the picnic basket." "That was clever!" said the rabbits. When the picnic was over, everybody crossed the stream through the hollow log without trouble this time.

17 The Good Seed

Long time ago, there lived a boy in China named Dink.

The king of that land had no children. One day, he announced that whoever grew the most beautiful flower would become his successor. Young men from all over the kingdom were given seeds by the king.

Dink too planted his seed. He took great care to make it grow. But to his dismay, even after two months the seed remained as it was, while his friends' seeds had grown into lovely flowers. Dink was very worried. He changed the soil in the pot and waited for the seed to grow. But a year passed and still the seed did not grow. The next year, all the young men carried their flowerpots to the king's palace. The king looked at all the flowers. When he saw Dink, he asked, "Why did you bring an empty pot?" Dink narrated the whole story to the king. The king smiled. He was impressed by Dink's honesty. The king said to the others, "The seeds I gave you all had been cooked. So it was impossible for them to grow. Only this boy has been honest. Only he deserves to be my successor."

18   The Mole's Adventure

Ginger the cat was excited to see a beautiful morning. "I shall go for a stroll and enjoy the lovely fresh air." So off went Ginger merrily.

She came across a tiny mole peering out of the earth. "Good morning, Brother Mole," hailed Ginger.

"What a grand morning, sister. I've come up from my burrow in search of adventure," said the mole. "What do you want to do?" asked Ginger. "I want to climb a tree. Will you help me?" "Moles can't climb trees," exclaimed Ginger. "But if you really want some adventure I will help you." Ginger thought for a while and had a wonderful idea. There was a swing nearby on the lowest branch of an apple tree. Ginger put the mole on the seat and pushed it higher and higher. The mole screamed in delight. "Oh! What fun I'm having." Meanwhile, Ginger quickly climbed up the other tree and grabbed the mole as he swung near him. The mole found himself standing high up on a tree! "I can't believe it. I've climbed a tree at last. Thank you, you have made my wish come true!"

19   The Just Punishment

A farmer once owned a fertile piece of land that reaped huge harvests. He was well off but very mean. He left his poor parents to fend for themselves. When they approached him for money and food, he refused. "Go away I have nothing to spare," he said. The old couple turned sadly away. On their way back, they met a midget who gave them a large chunk of cheese and some herbs to eat. When they ate the herb and the cheese something magical happened. The skies thundered and a huge storm swept through the town. Instead of their small hut, there stood a huge mansion. The couple was amazed at this and went at once to share the good news with their son. When they reached the farm they found their son lamenting his fate. The fertile land was no longer there. Instead it lay covered with stones and rubble. "The storm swept away everything I had!" he cried. The parents consoled their son and took him home with them.

20   George's Best Friend

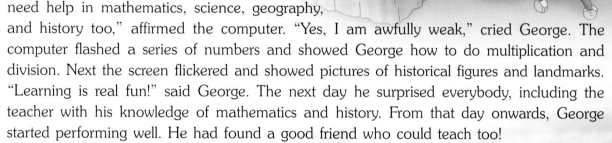

George was a poor student. His teachers filled his report card with bad remarks. That is why George had no friend in the class. Sad and dejected, George was sitting alone in his room one night. Suddenly his computer screen flashed, "Hello! George, why do you look so sad," said the computer. George jumped up in fright. "You speak?" asked George nervously. "I am a supercomputer and I can do anything," said the machine. George explained his problem. "Oh! You need help in mathematics, science, geography, and history too," affirmed the computer. "Yes, I am awfully weak," cried George. The computer flashed a series of numbers and showed George how to do multiplication and division. Next the screen flickered and showed pictures of historical figures and landmarks. "Learning is real fun!" said George. The next day he surprised everybody, including the teacher with his knowledge of mathematics and history. From that day onwards, George started performing well. He had found a good friend who could teach too!

21   The Little Green Tractor

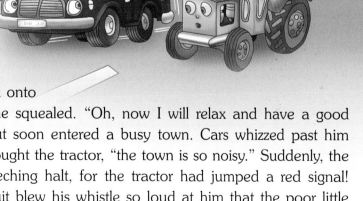

The little green tractor had been working very hard all year long on the farm. He was tired and wanted to go on a holiday. So early next morning, when the farmer was still fast asleep, the little tractor drove out of the farmyard and onto the highway. "I am on a holiday!" he squealed. "Oh, now I will relax and have a good time." He chugged happily along, but soon entered a busy town. Cars whizzed past him and honked loudly, "Oh my, my!" thought the tractor, "the town is so noisy." Suddenly, the vehicles around him came to a screeching halt, for the tractor had jumped a red signal! "Pheeee!" The policeman in a red suit blew his whistle so loud at him that the poor little green tractor was scared. He hurriedly turned off the main road and was back on the highway, "What a relief!" said the tractor. "My farmland is much better and I shall always stay there!" He drove quickly and came back to the farm before anyone was awake. Only Cock-a-doodle-doo saw. But he won't tell anyone.

22 Fluffy the Tortoise

Belinda's granddad had always told her that he would gift her a pet on her sixth birthday. "Whoopee!" cried Belinda, "I am six today and I will get a pet from Grandpa." "There is a duck with three little ducklings in the garden. How about one of those, Belinda?" asked Grandpa. "They are great but that's not what I want," replied Belinda. Next came the baker with two puppies. "Do you like these German Shepherds?" he asked Belinda. "How marvellous but I know exactly what I am looking for," she replied. So, Grandpa took Belinda to the pet shop. There were pigs, rabbits and colourful birds too, but Belinda didn't want them either. She was now sad as her pet was nowhere to be found. Just then a big green parrot swooped down and pulled off Belinda's fluffy hat. It dropped the hat on a tortoise, which was crossing the road leisurely. "Oh! This is exactly what I want," cried Belinda, "I shall call you Fluffy the tortoise!" and carried him home.

23 Wonder Girl Saves the World

Xelxis was a being from outer universe. She was a member of the Supreme Council, which safeguarded the Earth and all the other planets. One day her master said, "Earth is in danger of being destroyed by an asteroid You have to protect the Earthlings. We will change you into a human being, but you shall retain all your powers inside." In seconds Xelxis took on human form and was transported to Earth in a huge boat-like shuttle. She found herself in a school and looked wonderingly at all those around her. Inside the classroom, two naughty boys pulled her hair. Xelxis picked them up angrily and threw them into a corner. Just then they heard a thundering noise. "Asteroids!" screamed someone. Xelxis rushed outside and raised her hands towards the sky. Light flashed from her palms and destroyed the huge boulder-like objects. In a while all was quiet. Everybody was amazed. "Thank you for saving us. You are a wonder girl," said everyone. "It was my duty," said Xelxis. Just then her shuttle landed before her. She bid good-bye to everyone and returned home.

24 Eagle Ellen Needs Glasses

Eagle Ellen swooped and carried back a garden chair to the nest. "Another garden chair for breakfast!" cried her husband, "you must get your eyes checked."

"If I wear spectacles all the other eagles will laugh at me," cried Ellen. "The other eagles are laughing because you are getting garden chairs to eat," explained her husband. So Ellen went to meet Doctor Eagle. Doctor Eagle made her wear big glasses and asked her to identify animals drawn on the board. "Hippo, jumbo and giraffe," read Ellen. "See, I can read!" "That's great, now identify the animals in the second row," the doctor said. "D-o-g...C-A-T and umm," said Ellen trying hard to recognise the animals. "Your eyesight is very bad. You need good pair of glasses. Three dead mice for a pair of glasses," said Doctor Eagle. "But how can I catch three mice with my poor eyesight?" asked a worried Ellen. "You can wear your new glasses and catch them!" quipped Doctor Eagle. So Ellen got her glasses and never grabbed garden chairs ever again!

25 Piggyback

King Zach ruled the kingdom of Hackensack. He was so dirty and smelly that no one ever went near him. "Why do people dislike me? Is my crown on backwards?" he asked his minister, Sir Pack.

"That's because you are dirty and stinky," explained Sir Pack.

"What should I do then?" asked a worried King Zach.

"You should scrub yourself well and take a bath," replied Sir Pack. King Zach rushed to take a bath in the nearby pool. When he emerged from the pool he realised that he was once again standing in the mud, "Oh! My feet are soiled," sighed King Zach and rushed back to the pool. When Sir Pack arrived he explained his problem to him. "No problem, Master. I can carry you on my back," said Sir Pack. King Zach hopped on Pack's back and cried, "Hurrah, I will ride piggyback on your back from now on and my feet will never get dirty again!"

26 Matilda Is Missing

Matilda was Maggie's favourite doll. She carried Matilda wherever she went, neatly packed in her small bag. One day, Maggie went to the nearby children's park to play with her friends. She unzipped her bag to show Matilda to her friends. But when she put her hands in her bag it was empty! "Gosh! Where's my doll?" gasped Maggie. She sat down in the park and cried, "Matilda is missing. Oh, I've lost my doll." She cried so loudly that everybody in the park could hear her. Infact, her mother could hear her too and came rushing to the park. "Matilda is at home on your shelf. I had taken her out of your bag to clean her," explained her mother and handed Maggie the doll. Maggie wiped her tears and felt rather ashamed for screaming out so loud. All her friends laughed at Maggie's foolishness. Later, they sat around Maggie and all of them played with the doll.

27 How Joe and Sam Caught the Plump Pig

Pegs, a plump pig, left the jungle in search of food and water. He was so hungry that he began eating all the flowers, the grass, and scraps of paper littered on the road. But Pegs was still hungry and plodded towards the town. There he picked scraps from the garbage bin, pulled flowers from the trees and gnawed at the farmer's grain store. The farmer ran into his house and called the Pigs Patrol Office right away. Two boys, Joe and Sam, ran the Pigs Patrol Office. They were expert pig catchers. Meanwhile, Pegs knocked down the windmill and started a fire on the farm. When Joe and Sam arrived and saw the mess, they were shocked. "The pig is hiding inside the barn," said the farmer. "But he looks really hungry," said Joe. Now Joe and Sam thought hard and came up with a plan. "Let's place an ice cream box to tempt the pig. When he comes out we will catch him," said Joe. Now Pegs was a smart pig and he heard Joe's plan. But Joe and Sam were smarter, they had a secret plan. They went and took their position at the back door of the barn. So when the farmer kept the ice cream at the entrance to the barn, the pig crept out from the back door. As soon as he emerged Joe and Sam caught the pig with the help of a net.

28 The Unwanted Doll

Susie was once a beautiful doll. She stood in a corner of Mr. Brown's toy shop. Nobody bought her because one of her arms was missing. It was Christmas, the time of the year when children ask Santa Claus to fulfill their wishes. Susie made a wish, too, "Oh, Santa! Please give me a home this Christmas. When will I be loved by a little girl?"

That day many children came to the store with their parents. They admired Ted the teddy, Beads the fluffy dog and Bugs the green caterpillar with the dangling antenna. One by one they were all sold while Susie watched longingly from her corner.

Suddenly, in walked a girl on crutches. She looked at the pink elephant, the burly hippo and the magic telephone too. "I want that one," said she, pointing towards Susie. "She is pointing at me!" thought Susie in wonder. "But that's a broken doll," said Mr. Brown. "What will you do with a doll which has no arm?" asked her mother. "We can stitch it on, Mama," said the little girl. "Besides she looks so sad and lonely in that corner." "Oh! I should have thrown her out long ago," interrupted Mr. Brown. "Oh no, she needs to be loved too," explained the young girl.

Mr. Brown stitched Susie's arm and also gave her a new dress. "Oh! Look at her now! She is the prettiest doll here," said the young girl. That day Susie not only got back her arm, but also a loving owner.

Contents

The Story of the Month

Hudden, Dudden and Donald

01 Hudden, Dudden and Donald

Hudden and Dudden were two farmers. They had lots of livestock and fertile lands. But Hudden and Dudden were not happy, because they wanted more. Now, Hudden and Dudden's neighbour was another farmer named Donald. Donald was a poor but good-natured fellow. He had only one cow and a small piece of land, yet he was happy with his lot. The greedy farmers decided to kill Donald and take away his land. One night, Hudden and Dudden crept into his hut. However, that night Donald's cow was also in the house and thinking it to be Donald, the two murdered it instead.

Next morning, when Donald awoke he found his only cow killed. "What should I do with a dead cow?" thought Donald. He decided to sell the hide to earn money. Taking whatever little money he had he decided to set out in the morning. "What if the robbers attack me on the way? I will lose everything I have," he thought. So he made pockets in the cow's

hide where he put the pennies and set out for the market. After travelling for a while he felt tired and decided to halt at an inn. He placed the hide on the table. As he was eating, out came rolling a penny onto the ground. Then fell a second and a third.

"A hide with pennies!" thought the owner of the eatery watching them tinkle on the ground. Convinced that it was a magical hide, the owner approached Donald with a bagful of gold coins. "I'll pay you a bagful of gold coins for that hide," said the man. Donald was surprised but accepted the offer knowing that it was the best deal he could ever get. He walked home with the money rejoicing.

Hudden and Dudden watched wide-eyed as the man they thought was dead walked past them. They followed him to his house. Hudden and Dudden were amazed to see Donald take out a bag of gold coins. They asked Donald how he had got so much money. "I never knew people were paying gold coins for a mere cow's hide!" exclaimed Donald, narrating his story.

Hudden and Dudden winked at each other. They rushed back home and killed all their farm animals. Next morning, they set out for the market place carrying all the hides on a cart. "Farm-fresh hides for sale!" they shouted in the marketplace. "I'll pay you two pennies for one hide," bargained a man. "Get lost, you pauper, these hides are worth a bagful of gold coins!" boasted Hudden. "Ha, ha, ha!" laughed the customer and walked away.

"Catch those cheats!" screamed someone. They were soon surrounded by a crowd of people and among them was the innkeeper. "These men are with the man who sold me a useless hide for a bagful of gold," said the innkeeper to the crowd. "Beat the scoundrels!" he said. "Yes, now they are asking for gold in exchange for these cheap hides," confirmed another man. Poor Hudden and Dudden returned home with broken limbs, torn clothes and battered faces. They had lost all their healthy cattle due to their own greed.

That night they went to meet Donald thinking he would help them out. "Please have pity on us," said Dudden. "Lend us money to buy cattle, my friend!" begged Hudden. "When I was a poor farmer all you did was harm me. How can you ask me for help?" saying this Donald walked into his newly built mansion.

02 Mia and Roly-Poly

Mia, a lovely Chinese porcelain doll was sitting prettily on the shelf of a big toy shop. She had many friends. Aan, a Chinese doll, Shao a Japanese doll and also Barbie. But her best friend was Roly-poly, the teddy bear. One day, a little girl came to the store. "Daddy, see the Chinese doll. She is so pretty. Can I have her for Christmas?" Daddy readily agreed. But when the little girl tried to pick her up from the shelf she was surprised to see that Mia was holding the teddy bear's hand very tightly. "They must be best friends like Susie and me," thought the little girl. "Daddy, can I have the bear too? He is also so sweet," asked she. Daddy smiled and nodded his head. Mia and Roly-poly were very happy. "Thank you," they whispered to the little girl when Daddy was busy paying for them.

03 Picnic Food

Kathy and Timmy were having a picnic in their front yard. Kathy was arranging the carrot sticks on their plates when Timmy suddenly exclaimed, "Oh, we forgot to bring the lemonade!" So the girls quickly ran inside. When they came back, Kathy cried out surprised, "Timmy! Where are the carrot sticks?" Timmy said softly, "Kathy look! There is a rabbit near that bush!" Kathy and Timmy loved the furry white rabbit instantly. They fed it with carrots every day.

Soon it was winter. "Why don't we see the rabbit anymore?" asked Kathy and Timmy sadly. "Rabbits hide in their burrows to keep from the cold," explained Daddy. When it was spring, the rabbit was back again! And lo! She had six teeny-weeny bunnies with her! Timmy said, "Why, our rabbit is a Mummy bunny now!" Ever since, Timmy and Kathy had a rabbit family to take care of.

04 Sheikh Chilli

Once there lived a man named Sheikh Chilli. He was a simpleton but was very popular among his friends. One day, the landlord asked Chilli to count the total number of houses in the village. "I will pay you fifty paisa for each house you count!" the landlord said. Sheikh Chilli walked all over the village and counted all the houses and the landlord paid him as per the terms. When Chilli's friends came to know about this deal, they said, "Chilli! Don't you know that the landlord is dishonest? We are sure he must have cheated you!" "Don't worry, friends!" said Sheikh Chilli. "I cheated him this time! I counted hundred houses, but I only told him half the number!" Hearing this, Sheikh Chilli's friends had a hearty laugh.

05 Pamela Gets Ready for School

Pamela was very excited, afterall tomorrow would be her first day at school! Her aunt had gifted her a lovely purple sweater along with a pretty pink skirt. Mother had bought a violet bag and a blue water bottle. She switched on the lights in her room and looked at her new clothes. The bear on the bottle seemed to wink at her! "Oh, when will it be morning," thought Pamela. "Pamela!" cried her mother. "Are you not in bed? Please sleep, you have school tomorrow, darling!" "Good night, Mommy!" called Pamela. "Good night, Teddy. Let's sleep for we have school to…mor…row," she said sleepily to the bear on the bottle. Next morning, Pamela was up before Mommy. She got dressed by herself in her new pink dress. Mommy was amazed. Finally, it was time for school.

"Bye, darling," waved Mommy and Daddy as the big blue bus disappeared round the corner.

06 Silly Willy

Willy the goose was very, very lazy. He never liked to bend down and tie his shoelaces. He walked about with undone laces. One bright sunny day, Willy decided to go for a walk. He put on his smart new cap and shoes and set off. As usual his shoelaces were untied. At every street corner, someone would call out to him, "Willy! Tie your shoelaces! It's undone!" But Willy the goose pretended as though he did not hear them. Pulling his cap jauntily over his eyes, he went on walking with undone shoelaces! While walking down the hill, Willy tripped on his shoelaces. Rumble, tumble, splash! Willy landed in the dirty pond at the foot of the hill. Off flew his new cap and down it went in the muddy water. Poor Willy thumped his head against a nearby tree. Picking up his ruined cap, Willy waddled home crying to his mother. "Now, Willy, if you had listened to us, you wouldn't have hurt yourself!" said Mother. Silly Willy had learnt his lesson. He ties his shoelace every single day, now.

07 Sylvester and the Magic Pebble

One day, Sylvester the donkey spotted a red oval-shaped pebble. He knew that it was a wish fulfilling magic pebble and couldn't wait to show it to his parents. On the way back home, he saw a lion. Fearing that the lion would eat him up, Sylvester made a wish. "O' wish I was a rock!" And lo! The next moment he became a hard, solid rock. Now, he was safe but how was he going to become his old self? The pebble lay close by but unless he touched it he could never change back into a donkey. Sylvester's parents looked everywhere for their son. His mother was heartbroken. Tired after the long search, they sat down right next to Sylvester. Suddenly, his father saw the magic pebble. "What a lovely pebble. Sylvester would have loved it," he sighed and placed it on the rock. Sylvester quickly wished that he could be himself and the next moment he was!

08 The Magic Snowman

It was very cold. One morning when Sara woke up and looked outside, there was snow everywhere. "Hey! Henry, look! It's all white outside," she shouted to her brother who woke up with a jerk. He rushed to where Sara was standing and said, "Let's go out and make a snowman today." Henry and Sara loved playing in the snow. They quickly ate their breakfast and ran out. Sara picked up some black currants from the kitchen for the snowman's eyes, a moon shaped tomato piece for his lips and a red cherry for the nose. Once they had finished making the snowman, Sara said," He looks very good. I wish our snowman could walk." "Don't be silly, Sara. How can a snowman walk?" said Henry shrugging his shoulders. "Let's call Mom," suggested Sara excitedly. Henry agreed and as they turned around to go inside, Sara felt a cold touch on her shoulder. Startled, she turned around and saw the snowman standing right behind her. "I'm a magic snowman, dear," said the snowman winking his eyes and hugged the children.

09 Ram in the Pepper Patch

Once there lived a little girl in Mexico called Juanita. She worked hard every day and raised a patch of pepper. One morning, when Juanita came to tend to her patch she saw a ram happily grazing in her pepper patch! "Shoo!" she said, but the ram did not go away.

Just then a hen passed by and said, "I will chase the ram away!" But the ram butted the poor hen away. Then came a dog and tried to scare the ram away. But the ram was fiercer and scared the poor dog away. The big bad bull was proud of his strength. He too tried to chase the ram away. But the ram was stronger and the bull ran away! Then a little bumblebee came buzzing, "Little girl, don't cry! Let me try!" Hearing this, the ram laughed so hard that he forgot bees sting. "Ouch! Ouch!" cried the naughty ram in pain. He ran far, far away from the pepper patch! Juanita thanked the bumblebee and since then, the little Mexican girl and the tiny bumblebee became good friends.

10 Hiccups!

Alex Mouse sneaked up behind his sister Lucy Mouse to startle her and yelled, "Boo!" Ever since, Lucy has been having hiccups!

She tried all the tricks to get rid of her hiccups. She ate sugar, drank lots of water and even tried to hold her breath for a long time. But nothing worked. Lucy then went to her friend, Sam the skunk. "Sam...HIC...I have...HIC...hiccups!" "I noticed," said Sam. "Why don't you stand on your head? That always works for me!"

And so, poor Lucy stood on her head. But she kept falling every time she had a hiccup! Freeda the frog saw Lucy and told her to hop about patting her tummy. "That ought to work, Lucy!" said Freeda. But nothing worked for Lucy. Lucy walked back home, worried. "What if...HIC...I am never cured?" Just then, Alex sneaked up again and frightened Lucy. She was very angry. "ALEX! How many times do I..." Lucy realised that Alex had just cured her of her hiccups! They happily scampered back home.

11 A Fun Way to Fall Asleep

Charlie the little chimp had such a great day. He swung from branch to branch and hopped from tree to tree in the morning playing with his sister all day long. In the evening, he had banana shake with Dad. When it was time for bed Mom read a nice book to him. Now it was time to sleep. But every time Charlie squeezed his eyes close, they would pop open again!

So Charlie got out of bed and played with his racing car. But playing in the dark was no fun. He dare not switch the lights on because he did not want to wake up his sister. At last Charlie went back to bed thinking about what a great day he had. He began to think about what fun things he would do the next day... maybe read another book or eat banana casseroles and slowly, Charlie drifted off to sleep.

Now, that is a fun way to fall asleep! Isn't it friends?

12 The Smart Trader

Once upon a time, long ago, a Japanese trader went to China and bought six beautiful Chinese sparrows. "I will gift them to my king! He will love them! He will reward me handsomely for these gifts," thought the trader. But the king was a superstitious man. He always thought of the number seven as lucky for him. He was also known for his quick temper. Knowing this, the trader did not want to anger him. He thought hard for some time. He added an ordinary Japanese sparrow along with the six others, in the cage, to make them seven in total. The king was pleased when he saw the sparrows, but he said, "Hmm... I see that one sparrow is Japanese!" The trader was embarrassed at first but suddenly a brilliant idea came to his mind. He said, "You see, Sire, this ordinary bird is the interpreter, so he has to live with them!" Hearing this smart reply, the king was pleased and rewarded the trader a bagful of gold coins!

13 Waiting for the Train

During the old days when trains were new, everyone wanted to see a train pass by. Even Old Uncle Theodore, the old lion wanted to see a train pass by.

One day, Uncle Theodore heard two birds talking. "The train is coming from the west!" said one. "But I think it will pass only through the desert!" said the other. Theodore Lion wanted to see the train chug by. He walked for days in the desert to get a glimpse of the train. Not a drop of water he drank, for days! The two birds who had seen the old lion waiting, flew to the train and told the engine driver, "Old Uncle Theodore has been waiting for you in the desert for days now! All he wants to do is see your train pass by!" Now everyone loved Old Uncle Theodore. Hearing this, the engine driver fired up the engines. They rushed past the desert in top speed!

Old Uncle Theodore was now a very happy old lion.

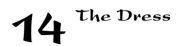

14 The Dress

All Mina wanted to wear for her birthday was her sister Tina's brand new dress. It was a lovely dress! Tina had not even worn it once, but Mina said, "We are sisters, right? What belongs to me is yours, what is yours will also be mine. So, I can wear your dress for my birthday! I will return it after the party!" Poor Tina! Daddy and Mommy were not happy with Mina. So, next morning, when Mommy and Daddy wished Mina, they gave her two tickets to Water Park, the greatest theme park in town. Tina gave her the beautiful dress and said, "Happy birthday, sis! This dress is for you!" Mina was overjoyed. She never thought getting the dress would be this easy. Daddy said, "The tickets should be Tina's since she gave you the dress. She can take someone along and have fun all day!" "And, I want to take Mommy with me!" said Tina, "I will return the tickets to you when we are back!"

Mina realised how selfish she had been and returned the beautiful dress to her sister.

15 The Pup That Wanted to Play

Bruno the pup was bored. He wanted to play. So, he went to Milky the cow and said, "Milky, I am bored. Please play with me!" But Milky said, "I am busy, Bruno! I need to give milk to Minnu!"

So, Bruno went to Rusty the rooster and said, "Rusty, I am bored. Please play with me!" But Rusty said, "I am busy, Bruno! I need to wake up Minnu!"

So, he went to Ozzie the ox and said, "Ozzie, I am bored. Please play with me!" But Ozzie said, "I am busy, Bruno! I need to plough the fields!"

So, Bruno went to Minnu's Mommy and said, "I am bored. Please play with me!" But Mommy said, "I am busy Bruno! I need to take Minnu to school! But sit here by the door and make sure the cat doesn't come inside!"

Bruno was happy at last. At least he had something to do now and wouldn't be bored anymore!

16 Super Granny!

Garry's Grandma can do anything!

Once two big boys at school bullied Garry.
Grandma picked up the boys and threw them.
They flew and fell twenty yards away!

Garry's Grandma can do anything!

Once two men with guns, tried to rob a bank.
Grandma used karate tactics and caught both of them!

Garry's Grandma can do anything! Once Grandma and
Garry were watching the news on television. They saw
that there was a fire in a high-rise building in London.
Grandma opened her umbrella, and along with
Garry, flew all the way to London! She then flew
to the top floors and rescued the people inside!
Garry's Grandma can do anything! When the
Queen heard about Grandma's deed, she said, "Well
done, Grandma! This is a medal for being so very brave!" When Grandma received
the medal, no one was prouder that Garry. And when he went to school next day, Garry's
friends said to each other—"Garry's Grandma can do anything!"

17 Reaching for the Stars

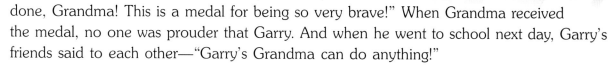

Lassie wanted to play with the shiny, sparkling stars. She felt it was better than
any of her toys. "But how do I reach up to the stars?" she wondered. She
lay in bed thinking. She could see through the window the stars smiling
at her from the sky above. Lassie walked out into the lawn. She
saw an owl sitting on a branch, and asked him, "O Wise Owl,
how can I reach the stars?" "HOOT! HOOT!" cried the owl.
"You must ask the brook!" So, Lassie went to the brook and
asked, "O Bubbly Brook, how can I reach the stars?" The
brook babbled, "These stars shine all night and I barely
get to sleep! Ask Misty the mountain." When she found
Misty, he said, "Climb to my top and I will take you to
the stars!" And so Lassie began to climb up and up
and up. She suddenly tripped on a pebble and down
she came tumbling! Lassie woke up with a start! "Oh!"
she exclaimed, "I have been dreaming all along!" Lassie
snuggled back into her bed and slipped into a deep sleep.

18 The Little Shepherd Boy

Eric was a little shepherd boy. Every morning he would take his flock of sheep and sit under a tree. He would see the village boys going to school. "I wish I could go to school like them," Eric often thought longingly but he knew that his father could not afford to send him to school. One day a young boy of his age came up to Eric and asked, "Friend, why don't you go to school rather than sitting under this tree all day?" Eric burst into tears and told him about his plight." Don't worry, I'll ask my father to help you to go to school," said the young boy and left. Early next morning Eric came and sat under the tree as usual watching his sheep graze. He waited anxiously for his new friend. Suddenly Eric felt a soft touch on his shoulder. He looked back and saw a man standing behind him. "Son, I'm Henry's father. Henry told me about you. You'll be going with Eric to school from next week," said the man with a smile and hugged Eric.

19 Peter's Birthday Bash

Peter was very excited. "It's my eighth birthday tomorrow. Can I have a birthday party with my friends?" he asked his mother. "Not this year, Peter. You had one last year so let's skip it this time," said his mother with a sigh. Tears rolled down Peter's cheeks and he wept bitterly that night. Next morning, he woke up late with swollen eyes and a gloomy look. He brushed his teeth and went down for breakfast. "Happy birthday, Peter," he heard a loud chorus. Peter looked around and what he saw surprised him. The room was decorated with colourful balloons and a delicious birthday cake was placed on the dining table along with a variety of snacks. All his friends were standing together with his parents holding a brightly wrapped gift. "This is for you," said his mother and hugged Peter. "Who organised this?" asked an amazed Peter. "This is our birthday gift to you," shouted his friends together. "Now open the gift and wear your new clothes," said his mother and they all laughed.

20 Doctor Frog

Freddy the frog was a proud fellow. He always boasted about what all he could do to everyone around. "I just can't stand Freddy!" twittered Tweety the sparrow. All the other animals were also very irritated with this habit of his. Whenever anyone saw Freddy approaching they would go the other way! One day, Freddy was boasting as usual to the other animals. "I am the most learned animal in this jungle! I am the smartest! I can cure every one of their ailments!" claimed Freddy. Foxy the talkative fox walked by. He heard Freddy and began laughing loudly. Tweety asked, "What's the matter, Foxy? What's so funny?" Finally, when Foxy stopped laughing, he said, "Friends take a look at Freddy! He can't walk; he hops! He has warts all over his body and he croaks! If he can't cure himself of his ailments, how will he help the others?" All the animals looked at Freddy and laughed aloud. Freddy the frog learnt never ever to boast to the other animals again.

21 The Miracle

Freddy was crippled from his birth. He could neither walk nor stand erect. His parents adored him a lot but Freddy was unhappy for he wanted to dance and play like the other children. His parents took him to every doctor in the city but nobody could cure Freddy. One day the entire Smith family along with Freddy's grandparents went to a lake resort for a picnic. Freddy was made to sit on his mat in the garden while the others walked around. Suddenly a little bug fell on Freddy's hands. Disturbed, Freddy wanted to throw it down. "Please don't throw me down. I can't survive in the cold," requested the bug. Freddy took pity and let it crawl down his legs. As the bug crawled, Freddy could feel a tingling sensation in his legs which he had never experienced before. Then all at once he felt a jerk and stood up. His parents rushed to him. No one could believe what they saw. "Good Lord, Freddy you can stand up," hugged his mother while Freddy looked for the bug. But it was nowhere to be seen.

22 The Story of Two Old Women

Once, there lived two old women, one was clever and the other a little foolish. Together they had one wrap, one cow and a small piece of land. The clever woman suggested, "Since we have only one wrap, you can use it during the day and I'll use it at night. Also, the front part of the cow belongs to you and the hind part is mine." When it was time to harvest the paddy or maize growing on their land, she said that the portion above the ground belonged to her. Now the foolish woman shivered all night. She had to feed the cow whereas the clever woman took all the milk and the crops. The foolish woman was quite unhappy. Seeing her plight, her neighbour advised her to soak the wrap in water, not to feed the cow and also to cut of the roots of the paddy or maize when they were still young. The woman did as she was told. Now, the clever woman shivered at night, the cow kicked her when she went to take milk and all the crops died too. At last she realised her mistake and mended her ways.

23 The Cat Who Loved Baked Beans

Marmalade the cat loved baked beans. But she was far too lazy to go to the market and buy them. She planted a bean tree in her garden and plucked the beans every morning. However, one day, she saw that the tree was gone. "Oh no! I have to go all the way to the market now," lamented Marmalade. "Why do you look so sad," asked the shopkeeper. "My bean tree is gone," replied Marmalade, "now I'll have to visit the market every day." The shopkeeper knew how lazy Marmalade really was. "Did you water it every day?" he asked. "I never do such hard jobs!" exclaimed Marmalade. "Did you weed her or ever talk to her?" he enquired. "That's far too much work," said Marmalade. "If you don't look after the tree why should she bother to give you your most loved food?" said the shopkeeper.

That day Marmalade planted another tree in her garden but this time she took good care of it!

24   The Witch and the Painted Helicopter

Froggy Witch woke up one morning and heard a nagging drone. It was Bob the pilot, flying his red helicopter. "Stop flying here," screamed Froggy. "No way, this is my flying zone," snapped Bob. "Abracadabra!" Froggy angrily waved her magic wand. And lo! the helicopter landed on the ground. Bob rushed home and brought many colourful paints. He swept green paint all over the helicopter. Then he added some purple dots too! "He, he, he," laughed Froggy as she watched the effects of her magic. Bob changed the colours of the helicopter—blue, yellow, orange, black! It had all the colours now. "People will laugh at his helicopter," thought Froggy as she swung her wand and made Bob steer his helicopter high into the skies. Happy that she had taught him a lesson, Froggy removed her magic spell. But lo! The wind blew away all the wet paint and Bob's helicopter was red again!

25   Dora and the Tooth Fairy

One day, little Dora felt something hard in her mouth. She took it out and to her horror, it was a tooth! "Oh no, my teeth are falling," she wailed. Mummy came rushing to see what had happened. Dora showed Mummy her missing tooth! "This happens to everybody. The milk teeth fall and new teeth replace them," explained Mummy. "Now, you must not lose this tooth," Mummy continued, "keep it safely under your pillow. At night the tooth fairy will come and take the tooth away and if you are lucky, she'll leave a little gift for you." Dora was very excited, she did as Mummy had told her. And guess what! Next morning, Dora found a pearl necklace under her pillow. "Look Mummy, the tooth fairy left a necklace for me," said Dora happily. If only Dora knew that Mummy had kept the necklace under the pillow!

26 Time Travellers

It was a fine sunny morning and Katie, Sam and Steve were on their way to school. Suddenly, Steve's dog darted in front of them. "Booww-Whooww!" "Oh no!" cried Steve, "Bennie is out of home again!" The children ran after Bennie. They were running so hard that they did not see the big hole. Thud! Thump!! All three children toppled into the hole and twirled down and down and landed inside it with a loud noise!

"Where are we, there's sand all around here?" asked Katie anxiously.

"Look! Aren't those the pyramids?" said Sam.

"That means we are in Egypt!" cried a surprised Steve.

They walked through a desert steeped in yellow colour sand and came to a place where many people were building a pyramid. "But the pyramids were built thousands of years ago!" said Katie. They had indeed travelled to the past!

"Who are you?" cried a soft voice. The children turned around and saw a funny little boy. He was wearing a white cloth like a skirt instead of trousers. His hair was long and black.

"We are travellers," said Sam. "Who are you?" asked Katie curiously.

"My name is Ramses and I am a the young prince of this great land," said the boy. "Come to my palace and have lunch with me. You must be tired," he smiled.

Off they went to Ramses' palace. It was made of gold and had beautiful stone carvings on its walls. Ramses' sister, Osi, welcomed them into their grand palace with a warm smile and presented the three little guests some lovely white flowers. Breathing in the beautiful fragrance of the flowers, all three fell into a deep sleep!

When they awoke, they were lying on their school lawn. "Were we dreaming?" asked Steve. Sam pointed to the flowers and said, "No, we were really travelling in time!"

27   The Blue Car and the Red Car

Mr. Peter had a majestic blue car. The car was very proud of his appearance. "How shabby the other cars look!" thought he when he saw the other cars. One day a new car came to the neighbourhood. She was a small red car and looked very pretty. A young girl owned her. All the cars were very happy to get a new neighbour. "Hi," honked one. "Welcome," honked another. But the blue car did not say anything. "Ah! Another shabby little thing has come," he sneered. But soon he felt he was falling in love with her. The new car was very sweet and she became friendly with everyone. The blue car felt jealous but he was too proud to talk to her. But one day he was very angry and honked, "You talk too much. I really hate cars who talk endlessly." "I love talking to my friends. How will vain cars like you understand friendship?" snapped the red car. The blue car was shocked. Never ever in his life anyone had talked to him like that. For the first time he felt lonely. From then onwards he tried to drop his proud manners.

One day, while Mr Peter was driving him, the young girl drove the red car and past him. The red car quickly planted a kiss on his cheek and sped off.

28   Nick Learns a Lesson

Long time ago, there lived a very naughty boy called Nick. He was a cause of trouble for all. He chased the girls and pulled their hair, he swore at old and young. Even the poor harmless birds were not spared. He hit them with stones and broke their wings. His poor mother spent her days worrying over what would become of her child. "Son, you should be a good and kind boy otherwise the goblins will punish you," his mother would often say. But Nick was deaf to his mother's words and continued with his bad ways. One morning, while he was alone, playing in the garden, the goblins came. They took him away to a faraway place. They pinched his cheeks and pulled his ears. Nick howled in pain. He begged to be taken to his mother promising to be good boy. The goblin chief spoke sternly, showing Nick what a bad boy he had been. From that day, Nick was a changed boy. He never troubled others and always listened to his mother.

29 A Friend in Need

Once upon a time, Slith the snail and Cousin Glug the slug lived in the shade of a cool, damp log. One day, Slith was trying to inch her way towards a juicy stalk. Glug soon overtook her. Slith tried to keep pace with Glug but the latter teased her, "Slith, you do know what is a snail's pace?"

Slith felt offended but a few minutes later when Glug stopped to feed on a juicy leaf, she overtook him and said, "There you are, one sluggish creature." Glug did not have a good sense of humour. He retorted, "How funny you look moving with your home on your back," referring to the snail's shell. But Slith kept silent.

A little later, they came to know from the ants that the woodlice had eaten the log under which they all lived and so now they had no home. But Slith's home was on her back! When Slith saw that Glug was worried, she said, "Friend, I won't leave you alone. We'll search a new log and make it our home."

30 Miss Moppet

Miss Moppet was a cat that lived in Mr. Brown's house. Slip the mouse lived in that house too. One day, Miss Moppet caught sight of Slip sleeping on top of the cupboard. Crouching softly she tried to jump on him. But Slip was too quick for her and disappeared to the other side. Miss Moppet hit her head on the cupboard. When Slip returned he was surprised to see the cat sitting in front of the fire with her head tied in a cloth. Thinking that the cat was ill, the mouse crept nearer and came close to Miss Moppet. The cat moaned. Holding her head in her paws, Miss Moppet watched the mouse through the hole in the cloth. When Slip was near, she pounced on him. She tied him in the cloth and tossed him like a ball. Poor Slip squeaked in fear. But alas! Miss Moppet forgot the hole in the cloth. She was shocked to see Slip chuckling merrily from the top of the cupboard. Once again the mouse had got the better of her!

31 Frank and the Fairy

Frank was the son of a poor village carpenter. Everyday Frank went with his father to the forest to cut trees.

One day, tired after a long day at work, Frank sat down on a log to take some rest. Suddenly he heard a cry, "Help me, please…" He stood up with a jerk and looked about, but there was no one there! "Please help!" Frank heard the voice again. This time Frank peeped in through the hole in the log and saw a tiny fairy inside. She was wearing a sparkling pink dress, had beautiful white wings and wore a gold crown around her bun. "Oh she's gorgeous!" thought Frank. "Please take me out of here!" she cried again. Frank at once put his hand inside the hole and picked up the fairy. The fairy thanked Frank saying, "Many years ago, a wicked witch had cursed me and since then, I have been trapped in this log. Thank you for saving me. What can I do for you?" Frank composed himself and said, "I belong to a very poor family and with the money that my father and I earn we do not even get two proper meals a day. So please make my father rich." The fairy's eyes welled up with tears as she heard about Frank's plight. "Boommm… Roommm… Zoommm…" said the fairy waving her wand and suddenly disappeared. "Where did you go, fairy?" cried Frank anxiously. But alas, the fairy had left!

That evening when Frank and his father returned home, there stood a palatial house with big iron gates instead of their thatched hut. "Where did our hut go?" cried Frank's father in disbelief. They walked in through the gates and were greeted like kings by the servants. Suddenly Frank's mother came running and hugged them and said, "God has answered our prayers." Frank looked up at the sky and imagined the fairy to be among the sparkling stars. He closed his eyes and said, "Thank you dear fairy!"

Contents

The Story of the Month: The Survivor

April

The Story of the Month

The Survivor

01 The Survivor

Long time ago, there was a tiny island in the Indian Ocean which was called Aranya. The island was ruled by a wise and good chief named Parvat. The island was beautiful and in the centre lay a beautiful garden which had trees and flowers of all shapes and sizes.

The island had an annual ritual. Every year on the first full moon after the rains, the people of the island held a grand festival in honour of their deity, Bhumidev. All the people dressed up in their best attire and gathered for the festival. On this occasion, the chief would select the most beautiful flowers in the garden to offer to their deity.

For the past eleven years, the rose had been chosen to be offered to the deity by virtue of its beauty and sweet fragrance. So everyone expected that this year too would be the same as the rose was indeed extremely beautiful with its double shades of red and pink. But the rose had become arrogant. It looked down on the other flowers and never allowed the bees and birds even the butterflies to linger on its petals.

"How proud the rose has become," said the butterfly to the sunflower as it sat on its petal one day. Soon the bees and the butterflies left the rose all alone and made friends with other flowers.

The rock behind the rose had a crack in the middle. Out of this crack, grew a plant with big heart-shaped leaves and lovely purple flowers.

No one knew the name or pedigree of this wild flower. Gradually news of this beautiful flower spread and the people of the town flocked to see it.

Like other years, the chief went to have a look at the various flowers in the garden—the rose, lilies, chrysanthemums, dahlias, and sunflowers. The rose was confident that he would be the chosen once again. All the flowers wished that this year they would be the lucky ones to be chosen by the king.

Suddenly, the chief pointed to the direction of the wild flowers and asked the gardener, "What flower is that? I haven't seen it before." The gardener replied that it was just a wild flower that grew on its own. The time came for the chief to announce the name of the most beautiful flower to be offered to the deity. The chief said, "Before I make the announcement, I would like to tell you the story of a poor orphan called Jwala. Jwala was a very hardworking and intelligent boy who wanted to do something worthwhile in life. On the island, there was a very learned teacher who taught the children of rich and royal families. Hearing Jwala's earnest request to be educated, the teacher agreed to teach him.

Jwala turned out to be the best and most capable student of all. Jwala emerged winner in all competitions and was chosen as the next chief by the reigning chief," the chief concluded the story. "And that Jwala is none other than your chief today. I have reached this position by years of hard work and struggle. Like me, this wild flower has also grown on its own without any pampering and care that the rose received. So it is also a survivor like me and I choose it as this year's offering."

All the birds and bees leapt in the air and flapped their wings in joy as their friend was offered to the deity.

02 Skip the Pirate

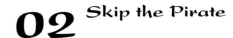

One day, Skip the pirate opened a treasure map and said to his helper Pip, "I have got a very good piece of news. This is Hippo Island where we will find a buried treasure chest!" Skip and Pip set sail towards Hippo Island. As Pip steered the ship, Skip said, "This adventure will make us very rich!" Soon the sea turned rough, clouds thundered and a strong wind swept over the area. The ship was tossed about on the choppy waters and landed with a thud on Hippo Island. "Hurry!" shouted Skip, as Pip took out the shovel to scoop up the earth. "There it is!" shouted Pip pointing to a wooden chest. It was indeed a huge chest. Skip and Pip pulled open the lid excitedly. But when they lifted the lid, out came a huge hippo! Seeing Skip and Pip, the hippo opened its wide mouth. Skip and Pip ran towards the ship and swore never ever to rob again.

03 Barry the Bat

Barry was a baby bat. Like all bats he was blind and scared of lights. He would not let poor Mama leave his side. At night when Barry went to sleep he would often wake up with a start. "The street lights are still on, Mama!" he would call out anxiously. "Don't worry, my child, we will go to a darker place," comforted his mother. So Barry followed his mother into a dark dingy cave. "But what if I feel hungry? Where will I get insects at night," asked Barry. "You can sense them by the sound you hear and catch them promptly!" explained his mother. "Now no more questions. You will hang upside down and fall asleep," said his mother warmly. "And will I get a warm hug from you?" asked Barry excitedly. "Sure, my child!" said his mother and gave Barry a warm hug.

04 The Black School

The Black School was run by the Devil. Here students were taught witchcraft and ancient magic. The school was located in a dark dungeon below the Earth. Many children attended the school. But the Devil had a strange custom—he would keep back a boy with him from the graduating batch of students as his assistant. On the last day of school every year, as soon as the last bell chimed, the boys ran up the flight of steps that led to the Earth, but the Devil managed to pull one student into the dungeon. This year too the children waited anxiously for the bell to ring and as soon as it did, they sprang up from their seats and rushed towards the stairs. One boy named Tom was a slow runner and the Devil knew this. But Tom was smart too. He wore a very loose cloak and as soon as the Devil grabbed it, the cloak came off and Tom ran away from the school.

05 Gifts of Heaven

In a village one year, the farmers reaped a huge harvest of wheat. All the farmers rejoiced and made merry at their good fortune. However, they forgot that it was God's blessing that had brought them this fortune and they became idle and selfish. One day, a young girl fell into a pool. Her clothes became dirty from the muddy water. Her mother hurriedly broke off a handful of wheat ears to brush off the dirt. Suddenly there was the sound of thunder. The angels who were watching from above had become angry. "You foolish woman, why are you wasting this worthy gift from heaven?" they scolded her. "If God becomes angry, He will not bless you any more." The mother realised the truth in their saying. She fell on her knees and pleaded, "Oh, please have mercy on us. We will die of hunger if you get angry and do not shower your blessings." The woman rushed back to the village to relate this happening. The farmers were scared and now took care to respect the crops that were their livelihood.

06 Borrowed Feathers

Mr. Peacock came rushing to Mr. Lion one night. "Please help me! I am being hunted down for my beautiful feathers by human beings," he cried. "I have a plan," said Mr. Lion confidently. "Why not dress ourselves as peacocks and scare the hunters," he suggested. "Excellent idea, Sir!" exclaimed the peacock. So the next morning, Mr. Peacock lent his feathers to the lion and his wife who covered their brown bodies with bright blue feathers. When the hunters entered the forest, Mr. Peacock called out loud to draw their attention. Mr. and Mrs. Lion walked past the hunters stealthily, "Oh, look what healthy peacocks!" exclaimed one of the hunters. As soon as they aimed their guns, Mr. and Mrs. Lion leapt forward and killed them. Soon word spread that the forest had huge ferocious peacocks who could kill. The hunters were too frightened to ever hunt peacocks again.

07 The Little Helicopter

The little helicopter ferried office goers to the city everyday. One morning, a pilot came rushing towards her with a van full of sacks and piles of hay. "Hurry up and pile these inside the chopper!" he said. "I hope she can fly with all this weight," said another man. "Sure I can!" said the helicopter. Soon the little helicopter was flying over a village that was completely flooded. People and animals were on their rooftops screaming for help. The pilot opened the door of the helicopter. One by one the sacks fell. Then he steered the helicopter and carefully landed on a narrow stretch of land. Soon people rushed towards them. They thanked them for reaching on time with food and medicines. That day, when the helicopter returned to its hanger, all the airport staff clapped and cheered it. "Good job done!" they said. The little helicopter no longer carried office goers, it became a rescue helicopter!

08   *Edgar Shares His Easter Eggs*

Edgar loved to paint Easter eggs. Every year he painted his eggs with bright colours. "Come Edgar, let's hide all the eggs in the garden for the Easter egg hunt," said his mother. "Mama, I won't give away my Easter eggs to other children," said Edgar anxiously. "Oh Edgar, sharing can be real fun too. It makes you as well as those around you happy," explained his mother. So Edgar and his mother hid all the eggs in different corners of the garden. Next day, when his friends came they had a joyful time hunting Easter eggs. After the game each child got one egg. "These eggs look beautiful," cried one friend. "So sweet of you to distribute your Easter eggs like this," said another friend. Edgar felt very special, for his friends had praised him. After his friends left, Edgar turned to his mother and said, "Mama, sharing is indeed a lot of fun!"

09   *What's My Name?*

Once there was a brilliant wizard. No one knew his name, even him! So everyone called him 'What's-My-Name'. He had the best spells in the kingdom. Now, there were three witches who were also living in the same kingdom. They were jealous of the wizard. No one came to them for spells because What's-My-Name was very good at his work. So, the three jealous witches made a very powerful spell of the winds and blew him off to Neverland. What's-My-Name wandered alone in Neverland for four days. At last he found a unicorn grazing in a meadow. It had a beautiful white coat and fluffy wings. When the unicorn heard What's-My-Names's story he promised to help him. He flew the wizard on his back and took him to his kingdom. What's-My-Name chased the three witches, in the three different directions, north, south and the west. No one was sent to the east because that is where the good witch of the East lives. And that was the end of the three wicked witches.

10 The First Messenger

Flurry was a little girl. She lived in a big house which was surrounded by many trees. One bright morning Flurry woke up and decided to go for a walk. Suddenly she heard a soft whistle. She looked around but saw nothing. The whistle sounded again. Now Flurry looked at her house. There was no one there either. The lilting whistle sounded a third time. Now Flurry looked at the tree. She saw a beautiful blue bird. Flurry leapt with joy. It was a Bluebird! "Where have you come from Bluebird," she asked curiously. "I was spending time in warm Australia. But now that spring's here again, I am back," explained the little bird. "And why do you whistle?" she asked. "I want to spread the news all over that spring is here!" said the Bluebird and flew off to another tree.

11 Yankee Doodle

Dolly asked her pet donkey, Yankee Doodle, to stay at home while she went to the market. Yankee Doodle was very naughty and after his mistress left, he went out for a little stroll. He crossed a fruit shop and took a mouthful of apples. The shopkeeper picked up a stick and shooed him away. After a while, Yankee Doodle passed by a park and started chewing the grass. The policeman, standing nearby saw him and chased after him. Just then, a band started playing Yankee Doodle's favourite song, "Yankee Doodle Dandy." Yankee Doodle followed the band and merrily danced away. As the band passed the market, Dolly saw her donkey and decided to teach him a lesson. She requested the band to go past her house so that Yankee Doodle would keep following it and she could take him home. Yankee Doodle happily danced along as he followed the band. As soon as they neared their house, Dolly caught her donkey and locked him in his stable. And Yankee Doodle promised never to disobey his mistress again.

12 Babe the Blue Ox

One chilly winter Paul Bunyan found a baby ox in the snow and took him home. He was named Babe the Blue Ox as the snow had stained him blue permanently. He grew up to be very strong and Paul made him carry logs for him.

One summer when Babe was hauling a load of logs he saw a pretty yeller calf named Bessie and fell in love with her. Babe asked Paul to take Bessie home with them. Babe and Bessie loved each other dearly but there was a small problem. Babe loved the winter and snow, since during winter, the logs would slide easier on the snow. But Bessie loved warm summer days. They went to Paul with their problem. Paul made Bessie a pair of green goggles and when she wore them in winter she thought it was summer. She was very glad and produced so much butter that Paul used the leftover butter to grease the lumber load. This kept Bessie and Babe both happy.

13 The Bicycle

David longed for a bicycle like his other friends but he knew that his family was poor and they could not afford it.

One morning, while going to school, David saw a boy coming on a bicycle. As the boy turned around a corner he hit an ice-cream cart. Crash! Splash! The boy and the bicycle fell into a dirty ditch. David ran to help the boy. He recognised the boy as the prefect of his school, William. William was badly hurt and would need to see a doctor. Thinking quickly, David picked up the bicycle and rode to the hospital. Soon the ambulance arrived to take William. David rode the bicycle to school to inform the school of the accident. Everyone praised David's quick thinking. William was discharged after two days. He thanked David for his help and to the latter's joy, William presented him with a lovely new bicycle on his birthday, later in the month!

14 The Magic Turtle

Whenever Hari was very sad or very happy he played his flute. Today he was very sad for he had got his school report and he had not done well at all! He knew his mother would be very angry. He wished he had listened to her when she told him to study hard. He sat on the riverbank wondering how to tell his mother about it. "Why are you looking so glum?" Hari heard a voice. When he looked up he saw a huge turtle swimming towards him. Hari narrated his plight. "So I've decided not to show my report to my mother," he concluded. "That's not the right thing to do. You must tell your mother the truth and promise her that you'll do better next time. It's never too late to mend your ways," said the turtle. "And don't worry," continued the turtle. "I am a magical turtle. I'll help you in your studies. But only if you play the flute for me every evening." Hari was delighted to hear this. He promised to come to the river every day. The two became friends forever.

15 The Story of Eklavya

Long ago there lived the Pandavas and the Kauravas, the princes of Hastinapura. All the princes were taught archery by Sage Dronacharya. The Pandava prince, Arjuna was Drona's favourite student. Ekalavya, a poor commoner boy also wanted to be Drona's pupil but Drona refused to teach him.

Ekalavya was a determined boy. He carved a statue of Drona on a tree trunk in the forest and started practising in front of it. Time went by. One day the princes and their teacher came to the same forest. As Arjuna aimed at a particularly difficult target, an arrow pierced the target. Shocked, the boys and their teacher looked around. They saw Ekalavya, who went up to touch Drona's feet. "Who is your teacher?" Drona asked. Ekalavya quietly led him to the statue. Drona did not want anyone to be better than Arjun. He thought for some time and said, "If I am your guru, give me my *gurudakshina*." "Surely, sir," bowed Ekalavya. "I want your right thumb," replied Drona. Ekalavya wordlessly cut off his right thumb and laid it at Drona's feet.

16 Gappu the Brave Hippo

Gappu the hippo was very sad. "Why are you so sad?" asked Jenny, Gappu's friend. "Everyone says I am fat and slow. No one loves me," said Gappu, a tear rolling down his cheek. "I think you are cute. And guess what, my uncle once told me that you can run faster than a man!" said Jenny Gappu cheered up and they became good friends. Jenny visited him often. One day, there was a great hue and cry. A boy had fallen into the crocodile enclosure next to Gappu. Gappu acted fast. He broke the gate separating the enclosures, rushed at the crocodile. "Quick, Jenny! Jump down on to my back. Lift the child up and ask someone to pull him up," Gappu shouted to Jenny. Jenny and Gappu saved the boy. "That was very brave of you, Gappu. We are proud to have you here," said the zoo warden. Gappu was very happy. No one ever called him slow again. They now called him Gappu the brave.

17 Granny Has an Idea

When Mr. and Mrs. Bunny decided to go on a vacation they decided to leave their children Edgar and Andrew to stay with Granny. Granny and Grandpa were very happy to see their grandchildren. Granny gave the two little bunnies juice, carrots and plum cake. When it was time for bed, Grandpa read them stories. But the two bunnies began to cry. "I want Mommy and Daddy," cried Andrew. Edgar soon followed. Granny had a brilliant idea to keep the bunnies busy. The next morning, she made them cut strips of paper and then paste them together. "See, this paper chain has five links. Mommy and Daddy will be back in five days," she said to them. "Every day we will break a link." This was an exciting game for the bunnies and they happily tore away one link everyday. And so the days passed till all the links were gone and there arrived Mr. and Mrs. Bunny. "Mommy, Daddy, we knew you were coming today. The paper link told us," cried Andrew. Mr. and Mrs. Bunny looked at each other in wonder.

18 The Gift

Meena was very excited because her Uncle Kumar was visiting her house today. Uncle Kumar always brought exciting gifts for her. Her father had gone to the airport to receive Uncle Kumar. Soon Uncle arrived carrying a big suitcase and Meena wondered what gift was inside it!

At night when her uncle went to bed early, Meena tiptoed into the guest room. Quietly, she crept towards the suitcase and slowly opened it. "Oh no! Books!" She was not interested in books. She looked further and took out a wooden box. Meena was astounded to see a sparkling diamond necklace inside it. "My friends will be green with envy when they see me wearing this beautiful necklace," she thought. She kept it back and tiptoed back to her room. That night she dreamt of the necklace. The next morning, she waited impatiently for her uncle to wake up. But she could barely hide her agony when uncle came out of his room and said that he had brought someone else's suitcase by mistake and was going to the police station to return it!

19 Bessie the Cow

Bessie was a strong highland cow. She lived in a big shed along with the other cows.

All the cows lived happily together except for Bessie's habit of snoring loudly. This disturbed the other cows who just couldn't sleep. At first they asked Bessie to stop snoring. When that did not work they warned Bessie and said that she must get rid of this bad habit, otherwise, she would have to leave the shed. But Bessie continued to snore and so one day she was asked to leave. The other cattle of that area wanted the shed too but they were afraid of Bessie. When they heard that Bessie had left, they thought that now it would be easy to overcome the cows. The cows now realised their blunder in asking Bessie to leave. They went to her and begged her to return. Bessie happily returned to her friends. She chased the other cattle away. Bessie continued to snore but now no one objected!

20 Dolly's Telephone

Dolly was a pretty doll in Tanya's nursery. One morning, when Dolly woke up, she was horrified to see her face covered with spots. She screamed in shock. "Oh my, what has happened to me!" she cried. She hurriedly went to the doctor who advised her to rest in bed for a week. Poor Dolly had to stay in bed the whole week. The other toys came to visit Dolly and tried to cheer her. They also brought flowers and chocolates and books for her. But after her friends left, she was again sad. She missed going out to play with her friends. Toy Telephone felt sorry for Dolly and said to her, "I can help you, Dolly. You can use me to talk to your friends for an hour daily. That way you will not feel bored." Dolly was thrilled to hear this. She thanked Toy Telephone for his help and quickly began to dial her friends' numbers.

21 Learning Good Habits

Neha was a very untidy and careless girl. Her room was always in a mess and she was constantly losing her belongings. Her mother would often say, "Neha, if you don't improve your ways, I'm sure you'll be in trouble some day." But Neha did not listen. Little did she realise that this bad habit of hers would cost her dearly.

Neha was studying hard for her exams. Often while studying she would discover that she didn't have some book or the other. She had to waste a lot of time looking for everything. The exams passed and everyone nervously awaited the results. Neha and her parents were completely shocked when the results were declared. Neha had failed the exams. Who better than she could have known the reason behind it. Her teachers and parents had repeatedly warned her to be more careful of her things. How could she tell others that she was not able to study well as she'd lost most of her books? Neha learnt a valuable lesson. She became more careful and paid heed to what her elders told her.

22 The Generous Crocodile

Once upon a time there lived a baby crocodile. He had a beautiful, shiny tail. The other crocodiles were very jealous of him and did not play with him. The baby crocodile was very lonely and was very sad. One day an idea struck him. He thought, "I have these beautiful scales on my tail but the other crocodiles don't. Maybe that is why they don't talk to me. I have a thousand scales. I can give away scales to all of them and make them happy." The next day the baby crocodile waited by the riverbank. When the other crocodiles came to bathe in the river, he timidly said, "Brothers, I have a wonderful idea. I will give each of you some scales from my tail. Will you then be my friend?"

The other crocodiles were amazed at the baby crocodile's generosity. They felt ashamed of their behaviour and promised to include him in their play.

23 Mike the Mixer

Mike the cement mixer saw some trucks and lorries lined up near a roadwork site. He asked one of the drivers, "Do you need some cement?" "No, we have enough of it," the driver replied tersely. Then he called out to a bricklayer near a building site. But the man said, "You're too late, we've finished our work for today." Finally he halted in front of a baker's shop. The baker cheerfully shouted, "Oh! You're just what I need. I'm baking the tallest cake in the world. Will you help me mix the dough as my hands will ache stirring such a great amount of dough." Mike was thrilled to find a job at last. He started his engine and the mixer began to turn and stir all the cake-mix. The mix was then transferred to eleven baking tins. Soon the aroma of cake spread through the shop. Mike was wondering who had ordered such a huge cake. He got the answer when there appeared a giraffe with the zookeeper! It was the giraffe's birthday.

24 Baby Lion Learns to Roar

Papa Lion lived in a jungle with his family. Papa Lion was worried. Baby Lion was growing big but had still not learnt to roar. What is a lion who cannot roar? Papa Lion asked the jackal to teach his cub. "Say Oooo! Oooo," the jackal said to the baby lion. When Papa Lion asked the cub to roar, he was very angry to hear his baby say "Oooo".

"Call the jackal," said the lion angrily. The jackal ran away in fear. Next the elephant was appointed to teach the baby lion how to roar. When he too failed in his mission he was chased out of the jungle. One day, all the animals were sunning on the riverbank. BANG! BANG! The sudden noise echoed in the air. "Run! Hunters!" screamed the other animals. Everyone ran as fast as they could. Baby Lion was so terrified that he let out a sudden roar. The hunters left the place in fear and his father's joy knew no bounds.

25 The Camel and the Pig

A camel and a pig were arguing as to who is superior. The camel said, "I'm much taller than you. I can easily defeat you in any contest."

The pig was quick to reply, "Nothing like being short. I can do wonders with my height which you cannot." Each decided to prove his superiority over the other.

They came to a garden that was enclosed by a low wall on all sides without any opening. But the camel was able to reach the plants in the garden with the help of his long neck. He fed on the plants and then turned to the pig that stood helplessly.

A little later, they reached a garden enclosed by a high wall with only a small gate for entry. The pig quickly entered the garden through the gate while the camel was too big to enter from the gate. He stood alone outside with a dejected look on his face. Both realised that all creatures big and small had their own advantages.

26 Elephants Don't Diet

Once there lived an elephant called Pluto who always looked sad. Her friend, Jerry the giraffe would ask her often, "Pluto, why is it that you are always sad. Tell me what's bothering you?" But Pluto didn't say a word and stood with her head drooping. Jerry asked the hornbill and the langur, "What do you think makes Pluto so sad?"

"Uhm, I think it's her long nose that hangs out in front of her face like a snake. Perhaps that makes her feel awkward," said the hornbill. The langur said, "I think it's her small, silly tail that doesn't allow her to hang from the branch like me." But Pluto told Jerry that her trunk and tail did not bother her at all. After some hesitation Pluto said, "Errrr, actually it's my weight. I'm so fat. I want to be thin like you." The giraffe was taken aback at the answer. He'd never heard of an elephant that wanted to become thin! "Pluto, elephants are meant to be fat just as giraffes are meant to be thin," he consoled his friend.

27 One Man's Horse

One day, a kind trader offered to take a poor, lame beggar on his horse. They rode together to the town of Basera. When they reached the town, the trader was taken aback to hear the beggar say, "Get down. Now this horse belongs to me." The angry trader argued in vain with the beggar. At last they took the matter to the judge. The judge told them to leave the horse with him and come back the next day. The next day the judge gave his judgement in favour of the trader. The trader asked the judge how he knew that the horse belonged to him. "It was simple," said the judge. "This morning when you were walking towards the court, the horse, which was kept in a stable, immediately looked up and neighed on seeing you, as an animal would react on seeing his master, but he made no movement on seeing the beggar. This proves that the horse belongs to you."

28 A Fishy Tale

One day, I was playing in my garden, all alone as usual, when suddenly a fish flew and landed right in front of me. "Don't be scared, little boy," said the fish. I was dazzled by its brilliant colours, which were reflected all over the garden in the sunlight. "Who are you?" I squeaked in surprise and a little fear. "I am the prince among fishes. I'm here to grant you two wishes." "Ah! This fish even speaks," I wondered. I had been longing for a puppy since a long time. I decided to try my luck. And behold, my wish came true. The prince of fishes gave me my best friend—Rover, the best dog in the world! Now I am never alone.

29 Chicken Licken

Chicken Licken was terrified to go all alone to the doctor. So he decided to take someone with him. On his way, he met Belephant and his sister Melephant. They wanted to accompany him but could not do so as their trunks were tied together. So Chicken Licken moved on and met Fish Finger and wished for his company. But lo! Chicken Licken was hungry and ate up Fish Finger instead. Finally when he met Felt Tip, Chicken Licken told him his problem. "I am a doctor," said Felt Tip. Chicken Licken did not believe him and pulled the lid of Felt Tip and threw it into the river. When he reached the doctor's chamber he was surprised to find Felt Tip's name written on the signboard. "I'll have to bandage it up myself now," he sighed.

30 The Fairy's Gift

On Christmas eve night, a fairy gifted Carl a story book. "You have one year to read this book. Next Christmas, I will come to take it back," she said. After a year when the fairy returned to take the book, she found that some of the crisp white pages had turned yellow and they had blotches too. Carl was puzzled. "I took great care of my book," he said. "The blotches appeared on the days you were naughty and it became yellow when you lied to your mother," explained the fairy. Carl felt very ashamed. The fairy gave him another book. "I promise you that this time you will find all white pages!" assured Carl.

Contents

The Story of the Month: The Good Turn

May

The Story of the Month

The Good Turn

01 The Good Turn

Gina was the only child of her parents who doted on her and thoroughly spoiled her. They fulfilled her every wish, however unreasonable. Unfortunately Gina grew up to be selfish and rude. No wonder the neighbours called her 'The Brat'!

Gina's mother had noticed on several occasions that Gina was not willing to share her books or toys with her friends. Moreover, she would bully them and quarrel with them over little things. Slowly, Gina's friends began to stay away from her. Soon it was time for Gina to go to school. Even in school Gina had no friends until Myra joined her class. Myra was a shy and timid girl who didn't mind being bossed around by Gina. She was not a bright pupil.

One day, Mrs. Brown the class teacher scolded Myra for leaving mistakes in her work. All the other children laughed at her, making Myra feel miserable. When Gina told her mother about the incident, her mother said, "Gina, you are her friend. You should help her." But Gina shrugged her shoulders and said, "What can I do if she's so dumb?"

"That is not a nice way to talk of your friend," scolded her mother. "Let me tell you a story about kindness."

Her mother narrated to her the story of an ant and a dove. Once an ant fell into a stream and desperately tried to get out of the water. On seeing the ant's plight, a dove who was sitting on a nearby tree, plucked a leaf and threw it close to the ant. The ant quickly climbed on the leaf and floated safely to the bank. A few days later, a bird catcher was passing by. Seeing the dove he tried to throw a net over it. But the ant saw the bird catcher. Remembering the dove's kindness the ant crawled up the bird catcher's arm and nipped him sharply. The bird catcher yelled in pain. This alerted the dove who flew away to safety.

"So Gina, did you learn something from the story? If you are good to others, then they too will be good to you."

Gina listened to her mother's words silently. The next day in class she helped Myra with her work. Mrs. Brown was pleased with Myra and praised her in the class. When Myra thanked Gina for her help, Gina's heart was filled with happiness.

One day, in a fit of temper, Gina beat up a girl in school. When the matter was reported to the principal, Gina was told to stay back after school. As a punishment she had to clean all the classrooms. Gina was dismayed. She was a proud girl and could not bear this humiliation. The other children giggled at Gina and made fun of her.

After school, Gina sat in a corner and sobbed bitterly. She was surprised when she heard Myra's voice. "Gina, don't cry. I'll stay back with you and help you to clean all the classrooms. Now let's get started."

Gina remembered the story of the ant and the dove. Her mother had been right after all. Gina realised how bad she had been to everyone. She decided to be a good girl from that day. Gina and Myra became the best of friends.

02 Why Hippopotamuses Live in Water

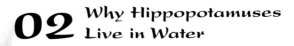

Many years ago there lived a hippopotamus called Isantim. Strangely, though everyone knew the hippo, no one except his seven wives knew his name. One day, the hippo invited all the animals to a feast. Just as the animals were about to eat he said, "None of you here know my name. If you cannot tell my name, then you all shall go away without dinner." All the animals looked at each other. As no one knew the hippo's name, all had to leave without food. "That is unfair," declared the lion angrily. "If anyone can find my name in seven days' time then I will leave the land forever!" said the hippo. One day, the hippo and his wives went to bathe in the lake. The tortoise happened to be close behind. One of the wives fell down. "Oh Isantim, help!" she cried. When the tortoise came to know the hippo's name, he ran to inform the other animals. The hippos had to leave the land, and live in water ever since.

03 Jumbo's Plan

Jumbo was an obedient elephant calf. He never disobeyed his mother and helped her with her work. But his mother was quite impatient and was always scolding Jumbo for one thing or the other. "Why can't I please mother?" Jumbo often thought. Suddenly he had an idea. "I should take care of Mom's flower plants. If I water them daily, she will be really very happy," thought Jumbo. Next morning Jumbo woke up early and went to the garden. He

filled the watering can with water and started watering the plants one by one humming a song:

"Oh my dear Mummy,
You can no longer be angry. When you see your flowers looking so pretty"

Jumbo's mother came out after a while and saw Jumbo watering her plants. "Oh, you are the best, Jumbo!" and gave him a big hug. You can imagine how happy Jumbo was!

04 Grandma Goes Flying

Amanda was a very naughty girl. Once when Amada's parents were away for a few days, her grandma came to look after her. One day Amanda threw a tantrum and said she would only eat it if Grandma taught her how to fly! She sat in a corner of the room and wouldn't listen to anyone. Poor Grandma didn't know what to do. Suddenly Grandma had a bright idea. She climbed a ladder to reach up to the precious chandelier in the living room, caught the chandelier and left the ladder. Lo and behold! Grandma went flying out of the window and fell with a big thud in the lawn outside. Amanda rushed out. "Oh Grandma, I didn't ask you to fly out of the window!" she said. Poor Grandma had to be taken to a doctor but she soon became better in a few days. Amanda realised her mistake and promised to be a good girl. She never troubled anyone again.

05 Pixie the Green Fairy

My name is Pixie and I'm a fairy. I live inside a giant mushroom. But no one knows this except for Amy, my best friend. My tribe has three types of fairies. The purple fairies are the queen fairies and live in castles, the green fairies are just normal fairies and the yellow ones are nurse fairies. I'm glad to be a green fairy because I'm free to do whatever I like. I was not always a fairy, you know. Two years ago, I ate this strange crab apple. The next morning when I woke up and looked into the mirror I saw that I was slowly changing into a fairy. At first I was alarmed. Now I am happy because I like being a fairy. I use my special powers to help my friends and heal them when they are ill. I visit Amy's house every night. We dance and play together and I help her in her studies. When somebody knocks on the door, I vanish like a fairy!

06 The Picnic

Hooty the owl was puzzled as none of her students had come to school that day. Only Wily the turtle had reached school. He liked going to school and learning new things. The other animals had decided to miss school that day and go on a picnic.

"I hate going to school to study," said Jumpy Monkey. "It's so boring," added Croaky Frog.

They were so busy talking that they forgot it was time to go home. Then they saw Wily returning from school. "Here comes the learned one," said Chirpy Sparrow, making fun of Wily. The others laughed loudly. Wily told them that he had learnt many new things at school that day. "Do you know the shape of the earth?" None of the other animals knew the answer. "It's round like an orange," replied Wily. "And tell me, what comes first, thunder or lightning?" Again the other animals were silent. They were now beginning to feel foolish and ashamed while Wily seemed wise. "I don't think it's such a good idea to miss school anymore," said Croaky. "Hurrah for school!" added Jumpy.

07 The Dragon Rock

Once in a faraway village there was a large, scaly rock that looked like a dragon. The villagers believed that the rock was actually a dragon. The villagers were worried because there had been no rains in the village for a long time.

"Help us, O' Mighty Dragon!" they prayed. Everyday, they carried flowers and placed them on the dragon. One day the sleeping dragon began to rumble and soon the low sound turned to a loud thunder. The land shook and heaved. Everyone stood at the foot of the dragon, watching wide-eyed. Before long, there was a heavy gush of water sprouting from the rock and flowing into the village. Though the village was flooded, no one minded and only thanked the sleeping dragon.

08   Joey Makes a Good Start

It's the first day of a New Year and little Joey is going to play baseball with his friends. "Mom, I cannot find my socks!" he yelled. Joey's mom gave him a stern look and said, "Maybe it's somewhere under your bed! And if you don't clean your room right away, you are not going anywhere, Son." Joey sighed and went to his room. He looked under his bed and lo! There were his socks! Surprisingly little Joey also discovered his paintbrush and his tennis racket under the bed. "Oh, I thought I had lost my tennis racket!" he exclaimed in delight. Then he scratched his head and thought for a while. "I am going to keep my room clean from now," he decided. When Mom peeped into the room, she saw Little Joey busy at work, neatly folding his clothes and arranging his scattered books, pencils and erasers. "You've made a good start to the new year, Joey!" said his mother encouragingly, "I'm going to make some chocolate tarts for you today." Joey beamed and went for his baseball match.

09   Look Who's Snoring

Maggie was usually a quiet, obedient girl but putting her to bed at night was always a big problem. While everyone slept, Maggie would stay awake. Daddy usually stayed up with Maggie. He played with her and swung her in the air and read stories to her every day. One night, after tucking Maggie in bed with all her dolls and teddies, he sat beside her and opened a book on fairies and read a story. Maggie was still wide awake and made him read three stories. Finally, Daddy yawned and closed the book. "Go to sleep, sweetie," he said and yawned once more. "One more story, please. I am not sleepy at all," begged Maggie. "No more stories now. Let's count from one to hundred," suggested Daddy, one...two...three...four..."

After a while, Mama peeped in to kiss Maggie goodnight. "Who's snoring?" she wondered aloud. "Sssssshhh," said Maggie, "It's Daddy, he's fast asleep."

10 Joseph's Overcoat

Joseph was a poor man who had an old overcoat. Over the years the coat became worn-out. Unable to wear it anymore, Joseph decided to make a jacket out of it. Joseph was happy with his jacket and proudly wore it everywhere. When the jacket became old, he made a vest out of it and danced at his nephew's wedding. When the vest was worn out he made a scarf out of it. With time Joseph's scarf turned into rags and then he made a necktie out of it. When the necktie was worn out, he made a handkerchief of it. Joseph always carried his handkerchief wherever he went. Slowly his handkerchief too wore off, so he decided to make a button from it, using it to fasten his suspenders. One day, Joseph was strolling down the riverbank and the button popped off. It rolled into the river and was lost forever.

"Goodbye, my friend," said Joseph. "You have served me well. I will miss you."

11 Kim and Ken

Kim and Ken lived with their parents in the State Zoo. Their father Joe was a zookeeper. Both the children loved all the animals. Everyday Kim and Ken would go up to the animals and play with them. Jumbo the elephant would pick them up in his trunk and put them on his back for a ride round the zoo. Ginny the giraffe would nuzzle their neck making them squeal with delight. But Kim was scared of the tigers. She would never go near the tigers' cages. One day, Mama Tiger gave birth to five little cubs. "Oh, aren't they adorable?" said Ken. Kim gathered courage and joined her brother. The cub rolled over and licked her hands. "Oooh! He's so sweet!" exclaimed Kim hugging the tiger cub. "See, I told you tigers are not always dangerous," Ken told his sister with a twinkle in his eyes. "Hmmm… I was frightened for no reason at all," admitted Kim and they both laughed. From then on, Kim visited the tigers every day and they rolled and chased each other and had a jolly good time.

12 Polly's Picture Album

"What's this Grandma?" asked Polly turning the pages of an old picture album. "This is our family picture album," replied Grandma. "Who is this baby in the tub?" asked Polly. "That's your grandpa when he was just a year old!" "And this little girl who looks like me?" asked Polly excitedly. "Oh, that's your mother!" said Grandma. "Oooh! This picture album is indeed a lot of fun to see!" said Polly.

Later that day when Polly went to her room, she took out a new workbook, painted it with bright colours and decorated the pages with lively stickers. Then she collected as many pictures of her friends and family as she could and stuck them in the different pages. Polly had made her own picture album!

13 Nowhere to Swim

The animals in Uncle Tom's farm were very upset. Their swimming pool had become very dirty! "It's hot but we cannot swim!" lamented the pigs. "How I wish I could spray myself some water!" sighed the old elephant. "Maybe we should have a word with Uncle Tom," suggested the hippopotamus. All the animals went to Uncle Tom who was busy washing his clothes in a big bathtub. "Uncle Tom, the pool is dirty. Where can we swim now?" asked the elephant. "The swimming pool will be cleaned tomorrow. Meanwhile, let me think of something," said the farmer. Suddenly his eyes lit up and he cried, "I've got it! I am going to fill this tub with water and all of you will get five minutes each to play in the water. You must stand in a queue and wait for your turn."

That afternoon all the animals had a good time in their new pool, splashing and splattering water!

14 The Lion Kid

Boomba was a very handsome lion cub. His parents were proud of their son's good looks. But Boomba was never happy with his looks. One day while Boomba was playing hide and seek with Polly the parrot, he said, "Wish I could be like you, Polly." "Why don't you go to the magic tree, Kalpataru, and ask him for help," suggested Polly. So, Boomba went to get himself changed. Kalpataru granted his wish. Finding himself all green with a red belt around his neck, Boomba was very happy till he met, Teeny, the swallow. Now he wanted to look like the swallow. He went to Kalpataru and became tiny like Teeny. He flew around happily and sat on Elly the elephant. Boomba then wished to become like Elly. But he felt very awkward because of his huge size. "O Kalpatru! Please make me a lion cub once again," begged Boomba. He was happy when his friends came and told him that he looked best as the way he always was—a handsome lion cub.

15 Our Big Universe

It was close to midnight and Jenny just wouldn't sleep. "Tell me another story, Mom," she insisted! "Ok, but this will be the last one!" said her mother sternly, and began narrating a funny tale about the universe:

"My handkerchief is in my pocket,
My pocket is on my shirt
My shirt is on me
And I am in my room
My room is in my house
My house is in a street
The street is in a city
And the city is in a state
The state is in a country
The country is in the world
The world is in the universe
Where a billion, trillion stars, planets and asteroids stay."
"Whew, if that's how big our universe is, then I must be like a crumb of bread!" thought Jenny sleepily and closed her eyes. She dreamt of sparkling stars, big planets, her parents, her friends and all the animals she loved—they all were one big happy family living in the big universe!

16 Ordinary Street

Mr. Black, Mrs. Grey and Mr. Brown were neighbours. They lived in the same lane in little drab houses on Ordinary Street. One day, the house next to Mr. Brown's became empty. Mrs. White came to look at the house but she found it dusty and full of cobwebs. Next Mr. Green came to buy it but he too found the garden small. On a rainy day a truck full of children stopped in front of the abandoned house. The whole lane was filled with their laughter. People peeped out of their windows. "Who are you?" they asked. "We are the Rainbow family," shouted the children and went into the house. The rain stopped and the weather became bright. Mr. and Mrs. Rainbow along with their children painted the house in bright colours and filled the garden with beautiful flowers. The house wore a new look. Mr. Black, Mrs. White and Mr. Grey decided to do the same. So Ordinary Street now became Bright Street.

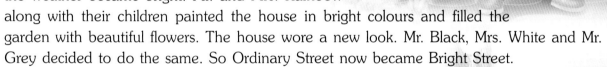

17 Ross and the Giant

Ding-dong-ding! Rang the grandfather clock at midnight. Thump! Thump! Thump! thundered Grisly Guy's footsteps as he came to town. Bang-bang-bang! He opened the door! Ha-ha-ha, he laughed loudly. Slurp-slurp-slurp! He smacked his lips! Ding-dong-ding! Bellowed the clock again.

"Oh Mom, the giant has come to eat me," Ross shrieked. "Wake up! Wake up, Ross. It's time to get ready for school," shouted his mother. Ross opened his eyes and looked around. "What happened!" asked his mother and hugged Ross. "Where is the giant?" Ross asked her rubbing his sleepy eyes. "The giant was in your dreams, Ross," she smiled. "Ohhhh," Ross thought, "but what if Grisly Guy returns again?" This time Ross decided to give him a tough fight in his dreams and packed his bags to go to school.

18   Salt and Pepper

Polo was about to go to bed when he heard a loud noise. He opened his door and peered into the dining room. "What's this?" he exclaimed. The salt and pepper shakers were talking! "Without me your food shall have no taste!" said the salt. "And if you don't use me your food will taste bland," insisted the pepper. The argument between the two went on and on, while Polo watched in amazement. "Let's ask Polo!" said the salt confidently. "What do you say, Polo, who is better among us!" demanded the pepper. "I can't do without any of you. If I eat a sandwich, I need salt and pepper both. But I also need mustard, sauce and cheese!" said Polo, "You must also remember that there are other ingredients as well which makes food taste the way it does!" The salt and the pepper understood how important it was not to feel too proud about oneself.

19   The Christmas Gift

It was Christmas. Mike was very excited. There was happiness all around and people were exchanging gifts. Mike was very happy today for Uncle Sam was coming for lunch. Mike had not met Uncle Sam for over a year.

Uncle Sam limped a little since he had had an accident a few years back. He used a walking stick now. When the bell rang, Mike rushed to open the door and hugged Uncle Sam. "Come with me, I have been waiting for you all morning," urged Mike. He led Uncle Sam to the Christmas tree and picked up a long box wrapped neatly and tied with a ribbon. Uncle Sam opened the box to see a lovely walking stick. "Do you like it?" asked Mike, "I made it for you in my carpentry class." Uncle Sam gave Mike a big hug and said, "Oh I love it as much as I love my little nephew. I am going to use it every day."

20 Professor Smart

Professor Smart, Jack's neighbour, was always busy inventing new things. One day while Jack was struggling with his homework, he saw Professor Smart pacing up and down in his house, scratching his head furiously. Jack had an idea. "I should ask the professor to help me with my tedious work," he thought.

Next time when Jack met Professor Smart, he said, "Sir, you are so clever. Why don't you invent something that will help me with my homework?" Professor Smart smiled and said, "All right, I'll think of something." The next morning Professor Smart called Jack, "Come here, boy. See what I have for you!" "What's this, Professor Smart?" asked Jack staring at the strangest-looking machine he had ever seen. "It is a full stop making machine," said the Professor proudly. Jack burst out laughing and said, "But… that can be easily done with my pencil. Never mind, I can use it for planting Dad's seeds."

21 To the Land of Colours

Nancy's was learning about colours at school. "Mama what is orange and how is brown any different?" asked Nancy when she returned from school. Mama took Nancy out to the garden and read her a poem about colours!

"The grass is green, the roses are red,
But the brown leaves are all dead.
The swirling sea is blue
And the butterfly has many a hue!
The morning sun is yellow,
For it is mellow
The bright aubergine is purple
And white teeth always sparkle!
Dazzling stars fill the black sky
And grey hair on mama's head makes her shy!!"

Next day, when Nancy went to school, she knew all the colours and had even learnt this poem. The teacher was very happy and gave Nancy a reward.

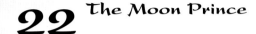

22 The Moon Prince

Little Roger loved to watch the silvery moon at night and wondered if he could go to the moon some day. One night, as Roger was watching the night sky, a silver ladder descended from the moon and a handsome prince walked down the ladder. Roger couldn't believe his eyes. The prince walked up to him and said, "I'm the Moon Prince. Come, I'll take you to the moon with me." Roger's joy knew no bounds. He quickly climbed up the ladder with the Moon Prince. "Wow! It's so… beautiful," exclaimed Roger when he saw the huge palace where the prince lived. The prince offered him many mouth-watering dishes. Roger sat on a big chair and ate the tastiest food in a silver plate. Around him were lots of sparkling jewels and diamonds. "Now close your eyes and think of home," said the prince. Roger closed his eyes and obeyed the prince and lo! He was home in his bed!

23 Dolly Learns to Make Friends

Dolly was a grumpy little girl. No one wanted to be her friend. One day, while walking to school, Dolly was hit by a speeding cyclist. A girl rushed to help her. It was Kathy, a girl to who Dolly had been rude many a time. With the help of two men, she put Dolly in a taxi and took her to the nearest hospital. The doctor advised Dolly to rest for a week so that her sprained ankle could heal. "I'll help you with the school work," offered Kathy. Dolly felt ashamed. She kept thinking of the past when she had never been good to others. "Forgive me, Kathy. I was so mean and yet you are helping me," she whispered. "I promise that from now on I too will help others." After that day, Dolly realised the importance of being good to others and of course, she learnt to make friends.

24 The Greedy Boy

One day a young boy called Pedro bought a loaf of freshly baked cheese bread from the bakery. The smell of the fresh bread made Pedro's mouth water and he could not wait to reach home to eat it. "Oh no! There is Bill."

Pedro was unhappy to see Bill at this time, as he did not want to share his bread with anyone. Pedro pretended as if he had not seen Bill but… "Hi, Pedro," called Bill. He followed his friend into the house. "I must hide the bread," thought Pedro. He asked Bill to wait outside while he quickly went to keep it in the kitchen. Pedro waited impatiently for Bill to leave. Even as he talked with Bill he kept thinking about the bread. As soon as Bill left, Pedro rushed to the kitchen. Alas! The loaf of bread had disappeared. Pedro searched all around the kitchen. "Slurrp, meow…" Pedro's heart sank when he saw the cat licking its lips. "I wish I had shared the bread with Bill. At least I could have got to taste it," thought Pedro.

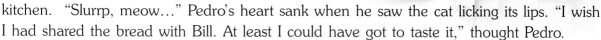

25 Betty's Birthday

Betty was very excited. She was going to be six years old tomorrow and there would be a big party. Next morning, Betty woke up early. "Happy Birthday," chorused her parents. Betty was delighted. Her mother kissed her while her father gave her a big hug. They gave her a gaily wrapped parcel. Betty quickly opened it and exclaimed in delight, "Oh, a teddy bear. Just what I wanted… I love it… I'm going to call it Brownie." In the evening, Betty wore her lovely fairy dress. There was a big cake. All her friends brought her lots of gifts. Mother had made pizzas, sandwiches and lemonade. There was ice cream too! All her friends were dressed like fairies as well and the living room looked like fairyland. Betty danced till she was tired. Soon it was time for everyone to go home. At night, Betty hugged her teddy bear and went to sleep dreaming of what she would do on her next birthday.

26 *Mr. Postman*

Maggie wrote a letter to her friend Wendy. She put it inside a lovely pink envelope. Suddenly, a gush of wind blew the envelope away. Poor Maggie looked helplessly as the envelope flew out of the window and disappeared. Maggie was very upset.

She rushed to her friend Gina, "Have you seen my pink envelope?" she cried. "No, I was busy feeding the fishes in the tank!" replied Gina.

Maggie then ran to the local bakery shop, "Has anybody here seen a pink envelope!" she yelled. "Is it the one which has pretty pink flowers on it?" asked a man dressed in a blue uniform. "Yes! Yes!" said Maggie excitedly. "But who are you?" she asked curiously. The man in the blue uniform said,

"I am Mr. Postman;

I collect your letters in my van

Come rain, storm or sunshine

You will get your letter always on time!

Crumpled, dirty, scented or whatever they might be,

Your letters are delivered by me

Do not worry young lady

For your letter has reached your friend Wendy!"

27 Why the Fish Has Scales

A beautiful baby girl was born to a farmer and his wife. They were wonderstruck by her beauty and showered her with a lot of love and affection.

The girl grew up to be vain and selfish. Often she went to the clear stream and admired her own reflection. She was always looking at herself and preening. One day, the king of crabs saw her. He was drawn to her beauty.

"Will you be my friend?" he asked her. "Oh, you ugly creature! How dare you think I'll be your friend," said the girl. The furious crab decided to teach her a lesson. He jumped at the girl and scratched her face. Shrieking in pain, the girl splashed water to wash off her wounds but those wounds soon became hard like scales. The crab king turned her into a fish with scales with his magic. Have you ever seen how fishes jerk away when they see their reflection? Perhaps it reminds them how they once lost their beauty.

28 Pretty Penny

One sunny morning, a little penny, called Pretty was sitting on her bed. She was very sad because she had no friends. Pretty Penny decided to go in search of new friends. A little later, she came across three pennies swimming in a pond. Pretty greeted them with a smile.

"My name is Penelope," said the first penny. "I'm Paula, this is my sister, Polly," said the second penny.

"Can I play with you?" asked Pretty.

"Sure, join us," said Polly.

So the four pennies played and laughed till it was evening, and time to go back home.

"See you tomorrow," said Pretty to her new friends.

So Pretty returned home to Purse Street, Penelope returned to Wallet Street while Polly and Paula remained in the pond.

Pretty happily told her parents about her new friends. That night they celebrated with a special roast of dollar.

29 Sunday Picnic

It was a bright and sunny Sunday. Johnnie went for a picnic with his mother, father and his little pup, Freddie. Cousin Tom also came along. What fun they had! Johnnie threw a red ball for Freddie to fetch and Freddie wagged his tail and played with the ball all morning. Johnnie and Tom flew kites together and even caught some fish. While Johnnie could catch only two fish, Tom proudly announced that he had caught seven. Johnnie's mother cooked the fish and they all ate a lovely lunch. Soon it was time to go home. Everybody joined to help Mother pack and clean the mess. But where was little Freddie? They searched everywhere but there was no sign of him at all. Johnnie was almost in tears. Just then, he picked up his cap from the ground and lo! There lay little Freddie all curled up under the hat to have his little nap.

30 The Flower Maiden

Penny loved to go and play in the garden. It was spring and all the flowers were in full bloom. One morning as Penny was sitting in the garden, she heard someone talking but she couldn't see anyone. The voice seemed to be coming from where the flowers were.

Penny went closer to the flowers. When she was near the tulips, she heard someone ask, "Who're you?" Penny nearly jumped out of her skin. "Err… I'm Penny…" she replied. She looked at the tulips closely and saw a tiny maiden with crimson lips and cheeks sitting on the petals of a tulip. "I'm the Flower Maiden and I live with the flowers. They wither and bloom for me," said the maiden extending her tiny hand. Penny smiled and asked, "Can we be friends?" "Sure," said the Flower Maiden. Penny was very happy. She now had a secret friend in the garden.

31 Two Moons

It was dark and the moon was shining in the sky. Little Ralph was coming back from a visit to Grandma with his family. On the way, they were walking past a pond when Ralph saw the moon in the water. He clutched his sister Susan's hand in excitement and shouted, "Look Susan! The moon has fallen in the pool." Susan burst into laughter. Ralph rushed to his elder brother George and said, "George, look! The moon has fallen in the water," "Oh! Really!" said George and his voice too choked with laughter. Ralph got very angry and went to his parents who were following the children. "Mummy! I saw the moon in the water," he said with a wonder. Mummy smiled and picked him up and said, "No, Ralph, the moon is still up there in the sky and what you saw in the water is just its reflection."

Contents

The Story of the Month

The Old Boot

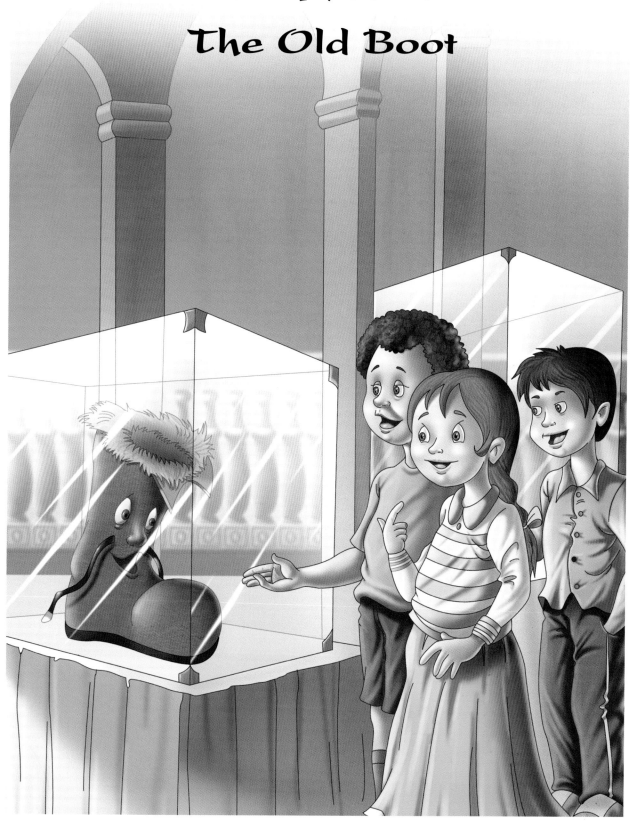

01 The Old Boot

Once upon a time there was a proud prince. He had many fine pairs of boots. There was one pair that he was most fond of. He wore them often. "These boots are as splendid as I am," the prince used to say proudly. But as the days and months passed, the boot started getting worn-out. The prince did not care much for it now. "Take this boot with you, I no longer want it," he said to his servant. The boot grew sad as it liked the prince and felt proud to protect his feet.

The servant was happy to get such a fine pair of boots. "I will wear it on Sundays while going to church," he declared. The boot was happy again to be made special. At first the servant took care of the boots but as days passed he became careless. The poor boot was knocked against stones while walking many times and started looking tattered and torn.

"Ugh!" said the servant to his wife one day. "I don't like these boots anymore. I think I will sell it to the cobbler." The cobbler took one of them and finding the other too tattered threw it in a marshy ditch. The poor boot grew lonely and miserable without its brother beside it.

"What a miserable life—from the palace to a ditch? Oh! How much I miss you, my brother. Where are you?" cried the boot in despair. All through the winter, summer and rainy days it lay there and thought of the happier times.

One day, a pair of tailorbirds saw the boot. "Look, wife! Such a cozy place to make the nest," exclaimed Mr. Tailorbird. "It will be warm inside," said the Mrs. Tailorbird. The birds made their nest in the boot and Mrs. Tailorbird laid four wonderful eggs. Soon the eggs hatched and the nest was filled with the cheep, cheep of the hatchlings. The boot was no longer lonely. He watched the little birds grow. Days passed and then one by one the little birds started to leave the nest till one fine sunny day the last bird flew out of the nest. Mr. and Mrs. Tailorbird thanked the boot and flew away too. "Oh! I am lonely and sad again," cried the boot. As it was wailing, a group of school children passed by.

"Hey! What is that?" shouted one boy. "Look! A bird's nest in a boot."

"It's so pretty! Let us take it to school," said another boy.

The next day the children showed the bird's nest to their teacher at school. Soon it was placed in the school museum. The boot was proud to be a part of the museum. "It is so nice to be here where so many children come to see me," thought the boot. "I only wish my brother too was here."

02 A Day in Bed

Last Sunday Little Tim had fever and so Mummy put him to bed. Ron came around to play but Mummy didn't let Tim go out of the house. "Get well soon," said Ron and went away to play with Dan. After eating lunch, Tim slept for an hour. When he woke up, he was feeling much better. "Please Mummy let me go and play. I am much better now," requested Tim. But Mummy refused. "I haven't been anywhere today," he grumbled. After a while Grandpa came to visit him. "How is my brave boy?" he asked. Grandpa was hiding something behind his back. "Have you got something for me?" asked Tim curiously. Grandpa laughed and held out a B-I-I-I-I-G box of Tim's favourite cookies. "Oh, I love you Grandpa," said Tim and gave Grandpa a big hug. "I don't mind being in bed now. I can eat my favourite cookies and I don't have to do any sums either," said Tim with a wink.

03 Marcus takes a bath

"Marcus, look, you have stained your shirt with paint again," exclaimed Mummy as she entered the room. Marcus was at his table furiously running his brush over a sheet of paper. He didn't even hear his mom come inside. "Oh no, you have ink all over your face and hands!" she lamented. "Go and wash yourself!" she said, "you must be careful!" "N-Nooo!" screamed Marcus. He hated having a bath. Mummy quickly thought of a plan. She filled a big tub with soap and bubbles and lots of hot water. Marcus was hiding under the bed. Mummy had to drag him and take him to the bathroom. She scrubbed him with soap and made him sit in the tub. "Marcus, I'll be back in a while," she said. Marcus stretched himself into a nice position and lay in the tub. "Ahhhh! this is not so bad after all," he thought. Guess what! When Mummy came back, Marcus was fast asleep! Mummy picked him up and wrapped him in a big towel. She pulled on a pair of pajamas and tucked him in bed. "I love you," said Mummy and kissed him goodnight.

04   *Jed's Special Sweater*

Jed was very fond of his red sweater. Aunt Judy, his favourite aunt had knitted it specially for his birthday. She had made a spaceman on the chest because she knew Jed loved spacemen. "It's very special to me. I love the spaceman very much," exclaimed Jed. Jed always wore his favourite red sweater. He did not even want to give it to be washed! One day, all the school children went swimming. "Oh no! I don't want to take off my sweater," said Jed. But, he had no other option. Jed took off the sweater and reluctantly kept it on a bench. After the swim, Jed quickly grabbed his sweater, wore it, and hurried home. Suddenly his eyes fell on something he could not even imagine. The spaceman was missing! "Where is the spaceman?" cried Jed. "Oh! How could I lose my favourite sweater?" "Mamma, my sweater…I lost it," wailed Jed. "You've worn the sweater backwards! Your spaceman is at the back," laughed his mother. "Thank God!" said Jed, happy and relieved to get back his sweater again.

05   *Squirrel Nutkin*

Nutkin was a naughty little squirrel. He lived at the edge of a lake in the woods with the other squirrels. "Let us go to the other side of the lake to gather nuts," said the leader of the squirrels, all set out for the journey. On the other side of the lake lived an old owl. Everybody respected the wise bird. "It will be fun to vex the old owl," thought Nutkin. Each day he would think of new ways to trouble the old owl. The owl hardly bothered about the puny squirrel making fuss. "Some day, I will teach him a lesson," thought the owl. One day, as usual, Nutkin was up to mischief when the owl suddenly caught the squirrel's tail and in a moment tied it upside down on a tree. Nutkin tried hard to pull himself free. He tugged and tugged and suddenly he was free. Alas! Half his tail came off. Even to this day if you ask Nutkin, "Where did half of your tail go?" He will sulk and say, "Tut! Tut! My bad behaviour took it away."

06 Why the Crows Are Black?

Ted ran to his mother with a picture and said, "Mummy, look at my picture." "This is really beautiful, but what is that white bird you have painted?" asked Mummy. "It is a crow. I don't like a black crow. So I have painted it white," explained Ted. Mummy laughed and said, "Well, there was a time when crows were actually white." And she started telling a story, "A long time ago, the Sun asked a crow to deliver a ruby which he had put into a silken bag for his beloved, who was a princess on Earth. While passing over a village, the crow felt hungry and decided to stop for a while. He hung the bag on a small branch of a tree and flew off in search of some food. Meanwhile a merchant noticed the bag and pocketed the ruby. Instead, he put some rubbish in the bag. When the crow took the bag to the princess, she saw the rubbish in the bag and became furious. Later, when the Sun came to know what had happened, he was so angry that under his burning glare all the feathers of the crow got scorched and turned black."

07 The Banquet

Once upon a time there was an old man who lived all alone in a small cottage near the woods. His daughter who lived in the city worried about him and would tell him to come over to the city, but every time the old man would say that he couldn't leave his neighbours alone in the harsh winter. That morning when he was about to go out of his house to collect wood, he saw a thick layer of snow outside. The old man put on his jacket and gloves and picking up a shovel he cleared the snow. Then he began with his preparations for the banquet for his winter friends. After preparing some delicious food he sat on his armchair and waited for his friends to arrive. The first to come were the red cardinals and the robins. They eagerly rushed to the feeders for breakfast. Soon there were blue jays, squirrels and mice all grabbing their share of the breakfast. A few deer also arrived and fed on the dried corn that was kept in the backyard. Meanwhile the old man's daughter called up and asked him, "Father, what are you doing in the cold?" "I'm having breakfast with my neighbours," he said.

08 The Sundrop

The ground was covered with snow. A little flower, still inside its bulb, longed to come out of the snowy ground and bloom.

One day, it rained and the water trickled down the snow under the ground and a delicate ray of light pierced through the ground and touched the bulb. The flower loved the sun's warmth after a long spell of chilly weather. "Come in lovely Sunbeam," said the bulb. "I'm not strong enough to come right now. I'll be much stronger in spring, little flower," replied the sunbeam.

"But spring is far away. I feel so cramped and chilly. I want to look out and say good morning to everyone," said the flower. The sunbeam's heart reached out to the flower. Its rays became stronger and the little flower pushed hard and finally popped out of its bulb, raised its head from the snow and bloomed pure and white.

"Oh, look at that lovely sundrop," exclaimed a little girl to her friend. The sundrop bloomed even more to express its happiness.

09 The Polecat from Top Hill

There lived a fuzzy and foul-smelling polecat on Top Hill. "Run away! Here comes the filthy and smelly polecat!" warned the other creatures. As soon as the polecat arrived, all the other animals would cover their noses and run for cover.

One day a big hungry tiger came to Top Hill and threatened to eat all the animals. "What should we do now!" wondered the anxious animals. "Can I help?" asked the polecat softly. "Sure you can!" nodded the animals smilingly.

The next day the polecat went to meet the tiger. The tiger shrank back from its bad odour. Nearly fainting from the strong smell, the tiger ran away and never returned to Top Hill.

10 The Four Wives

A rich merchant had four wives. He showered his first wife with valuable gifts for she was very beautiful. His second wife belonged to a very rich family, so he took her along to meet kings and famous people. His third wife was very educated and she often gave him advice on his business. However, he neglected his fourth wife who was neither beautiful nor very educated. But she was a kind human being.

Misfortune struck the merchant and he lost all his property and became a pauper. The first three wives immediately deserted him. Only the fourth wife remained with him. Now the merchant realised his mistake. He said to his fourth wife, "I was a foolish man and didn't know that after all a good heart matters more than looks, wealth or education!"

11 Small Good Wolf

Willy the small good wolf was the grandson of Big Bad Wolf. His grandfather had been killed by the goat family. One day, he decided to dress up in a lion's costume to scare the three goats who lived near his den. On hearing his roars, the three goats loaded their blowpipes with darts and came out of their house. Seeing the goats charging towards him, the wolf was scared and hid among the bushes. He stayed hidden for a long time. He then decided it was better to forget the past and become friends with the goats. He went to the goats and invited them for the Christmas party. The goats readily agreed. Everyone had a wonderful time together.

12   The New Neighbours

Steve was the only child of his parents. Often, he longed for friends with whom he could play. "There's a new family next door," said Steve's mother one day. Though Steve longed to meet the new family, he was shy. The next day after the school bell rang, all the children rushed out of their classrooms. Steve ran to meet his mother at the school gate. He looked everywhere but could not see her. Slowly he walked home alone but there was no one to answer the bell. He sat on the steps wondering what to do. Just as he was about to go to the nearby grocery shop where his father worked, he heard his neighbour, Mr. Smith's voice. Mr. Smith told Steve that his mother had been called away urgently. "Stay with us till she comes back," he said. Steve made friends with their son, Johnny and their dog, Rover. They played happily till his mother returned. Soon it was time to go home. Steve said goodbye after promising to come everyday.

13   Larry and Harry

Larry was a fuzzy old dog and his best friend was Harry the frog. Now Harry was very naughty and fidgety. He would hop from one corner of the house to the other, sling from the ceiling fan or swing on the chandelier. The children in the neighbourhood were always worried for they never knew from which direction or on whose head the frisky frog would jump on. "Why can't you sit in one place!" said an angry Larry, "yesterday my good old neighbour complained how you jumped from the roof and dashed against her glass window!" "Oh! Larry please don't get annoyed. The mosquitoes swirling around me keep troubling me," replied Harry "Oh! My poor little frog, I shall help you solve the problem!" said Larry. "Sit on my back and I will fan you with my tail." The two friends were happy again.

14 The Clever Farmer

One day a king was touring his kingdom on his horse when he saw a farmer working in his maize field. The fertile land attracted the king's attention and he wanted to procure it. The farmer owned the land and so it was not easy for the king to announce it as his. He called the farmer and said "You must come to my court tomorrow. But remember you'll have to come riding and walking at the same time. If you fail to do so then your land shall be taken away from you." The farmer was very clever. Next day he sat on a he-goat and went to the king's court dragging his feet on the ground. When the king saw him riding and walking at the same time he realised that he had been outsmarted. The king then came up with another plan. "Tomorrow meet me in this court without your clothes but dressed at the same time." The farmer smiled and went away. Next morning, he borrowed a big fishing net from his friend and draped himself in it. So there he was without his clothes on but still fully dressed. When the king saw him, he was furious and gave up his plan to grab the land.

15 Polly Helps a Friend

Little Polly loved to play on the slide. She would hastily climb its steps and smoothly glide down its slanted platform. One evening when Polly was about to climb the slide, she heard a loud shriek. "Ouch that hurts!" said a strange voice. Not able to see anyone, Polly placed her feet on the slide again when it shook so hard that she almost fell. "Stop, I say!" said the same strange voice. "Is that you, Slide?" asked Polly anxiously. "Yes, it's me the poor old slide who has been endlessly stamped, kicked, pulled and pushed by you naughty children." "Oh! I'm so sorry," said Polly and inspected the slide's cracked frame. "You indeed need a good repair!" she reasoned. Next day, Polly brought a carpenter to repair the slide and painted it with bright colours, "Thank you for helping me, Polly!" said the slide and let Polly and her friends climb its back once again.

16 The Frog with Three Legs

A little frog called Tri-Boy had three hind legs. The other frogs teased him because he looked funny and different from them. One day, all the frogs decided to go on a picnic to Farmer Brown's animal farm. They reluctantly included Tri-Boy in the picnic. They had just gone a little way when they all fell into the pit that Framer Brown had prepared for the foxes and other predators that came to attack his chickens. "What shall we do now? Farmer Brown will find us and fry us for dinner," said the eldest frog. The frogs tried to jump high to get out of the pit but failed. But Tri-boy's third hind leg helped him to jump much higher and he was able to come out, much to the amazement of all. He quickly brought a long stick and dropped it into the pit. The frogs climbed up the stick and finally escaped from the pit. Everyone rejoiced and thanked Tri-Boy for saving them. Then on, the other frogs always looked up to Tri-Boy.

17 The Owl and the Pussy Cat

The Owl and the Pussy Cat were very much in love. One day, they decided to go on a voyage to the sea. They set out on a pretty green boat on a lovely moonlit night. "Dear, isn't it a glorious night? Just meant for us," the Owl said to the Pussy Cat. They carried some honey and some money. They rowed on and on and the Owl sang for his beloved as he played on his small guitar. "Oh my lovely Pussy, how much I love you." The cat looked up at the stars and closed her eyes and saw sweet dreams. The Pussy said, "My handsome Owl. You sing so elegantly. Let's marry, dear. We've waited so long. But from where will we get the ring?" So they sailed away to Dreamland where golden trees grew and birds sang the whole day. There they asked a pink and plump pig who had a ring at the end of his nose, "Friend Piggy, would you sell us that ring on your nose for a shilling?" "I will," replied the pig in a singing tone. So they took the ring and were married the next day. They dined on mince meat and cheese and danced hand in hand till they were so tired that they decided to sleep.

18 Giant Jimmy Jones

Once there lived in the high mountains a giant called Jimmy Jones. Jimmy was a good-hearted giant loved by all. One day, Giant Jimmy Jones said to the villagers, "I want to go for a walk around the world but I don't have shoes." "We can ask the carpenter to make giant wooden shoes," suggested an old man.

"Or we could knit giant woollen shoes for Jimmy," said a stout woman. "All this would take time. Jimmy wants his shoes by tomorrow," said the mayor. Just then a little boy said, "Jimmy could use my uncle's two old fishing boats."

"That's a great idea," said Jimmy.

The next morning, Jimmy slipped his feet into the fishing boats and happily set off for his walk around the world. He was back in the village for dinner after walking around the world.

19 The Bucket with a Hole

Betty loved the seaside. Once her uncle invited Betty and her parents to stay at his seaside cottage. Every day she would carry water from the sea in her bright blue bucket and then pour it into a deep hole that she had found near her uncle's cottage.

One day Betty found a hole in the bucket. She was disappointed and left the bucket on the beach.

The next day, Betty returned home as her holidays were over. The bright blue bucket was sad at being left alone. "I'm of no use," thought the bucket sadly.

After a few days, a little boy was playing on the beach. He saw the bright blue bucket. He didn't seem to mind the hole in the bucket.

"You're just what I need," he said delightedly. For the rest of the summer, the little boy played with the bucket. When it was time to go home he took the bucket with him.

20 Old Benjamin and his Beard

Old Benjamin was known for two things, one was his long beard which touched his knee and the other was his habit of snoring. His neighbours didn't know what to do with Benjamin. Every night, he would snore so loudly that the entire neighbourhood couldn't sleep. One day Benjamin's grandson went up to him and said, "Grandpa, when you sleep do you keep your beard under the blanket or do you keep it on the blanket?" Benjamin was baffled by this innocent question. He caressed his beard, scratched his head but didn't know what to say. "It's so strange that I haven't thought about it ever," wondered Benjamin. That night, he got into bed and pulled the blanket over himself. First he kept his beard under his blanket. Then he felt that something was not quite right with the arrangement and took it out of the blanket. This went on through out the night and for the first time in his life, Old Benjamin spent a sleepless night and his family and neighbours slept peacefully. Next morning, Benjamin decided to get rid of his beard!

21 A Shelf Full of Dolls

Sarah's father was a pilot. He travelled to new countries every day. He would always bring dolls for Sarah from different countries. Sarah loved her collection of dolls and kept them neatly on a shelf in her room. One day Dad said, "Sarah, you'll need a new shelf in your room." "Why Dad? I already have two huge shelves." Her father smiled and left for his next trip. Sarah asked her mother but she only smiled mysteriously. When Dad returned from his trip, Sarah watched him take out a big case with a strange looking new doll made from painted wood. Seeing Sarah's confused look, her father said, "This is a Russian doll. You can actually unscrew its body." Sarah cried excitedly, "Look, Mama," as she unscrewed the body of the doll. She found another doll inside it and another when she unscrewed the second. There were ten dolls inside the big doll, each smaller than the other! "Thank you, Daddy!" Sarah hugged her father as they together put the ten dolls on the new long shelf.

22 The Man Who Loved Bread

Once there lived a man who loved eating bread. He had bread for breakfast, lunch and dinner and whenever he felt hungry. One day he went to a restaurant and ordered for bread and butter. After finishing it, the man ordered for a loaf, then another, and then another and soon the restaurant ran short of bread. The man told the waiter, 'The next time I come here, I'll expect you to keep lots of bread." On his second visit to the restaurant the waiter served him with double the number of loaves he had on his last visit. Yet, the man was unhappy! A few days later the man came again. The cook informed the bakery and the latter delivered a gigantic loaf over 6 feet long, 3 feet wide and 4 feet thick. The waiter and the cook proudly took it to the man. But quite contrary to their expectations, the man threw away his plate and screamed, "How many times do I have to tell you that I need lots of bread and just not ONE loaf!!!"

23 Cats and Rats

Matthew loves watching the Tom and Jerry show. Of the two, he loves Jerry more. "But why is Tom always mad at Jerry?" Matthew asked his Mummy. "Well, cats and rats don't like each other," said Mummy and started telling a story, "A long time ago the emperor of China organised a race among the animals and birds. The first twelve were to be given a place in the Chinese Zodiac signs and each would have a year named after him. All the animals practised hard for the race. But the cat and the rat were very lazy and didn't bother. Even on the final day, they were sleeping. The ox, being very helpful tried hard to wake them up, but failed. Unwilling to leave them, he managed to take them on his back and started running. Just as he was about to cross the last hurdle, a river, the rat opened his eyes. He sensed that he did stand a chance to come in the first twelve. Knowing very well that he would never beat the cat in the race, he knocked him off the ox's back. And when the ox reached the other side, the rat jumped off and scampered away to victory. So the Chinese Zodiac cycle starts with the rat and the ox following him. Poor cat! Obviously he wasn't anywhere in the first twelve. Since then cats and rats are enemies."

24 Mr. Maggs and Monty

Mr. Maggs had a big dog named Monty, who loved to go for long walks. Monty had long legs and walked so fast that Mr. Maggs had to run to keep pace with his dog. He had to tightly hold on to his scarf and hat, so that they would not fall off while he ran. One evening Mr. Maggs went to the market leaving Monty at home. When he returned Monty saw that his master had a huge parcel in his hand, "What would this be?" thought Monty curiously. Next morning Monty leapt out and ran fast as usual, but Mr. Maggs was surprisingly right behind his dog, whizzing along! So, Monty stopped and looked around. And guess what he saw? Mr. Maggs was wearing roller skates! "So that's what was in the mysterious parcel?" thought Monty and happily ran again.

25 The Magician

One hot day, twelve sisters, who lived in a village in Africa, went for a swim to the river nearby. While they were having fun in the water, a man came by and sat by the riverside. He picked up a scarf from the lot that the sisters had left on the bank and said, "If she who owns the scarf wants this back, she must bring me some thorns." On hearing this, the girl to whom the scarf belonged collected some thorns and gave them to the man. And lo! She turned into a thorn bush. Her sisters saw what had happened and ran away in fright. A magician, seeing the plight of the girl brought her back to her earlier form. "I am sure one of my errant students has done this. Don't worry I'll teach him a lesson," said he. The magician told all the sisters to go to the river again and leave their scarves on the riverbank. This time when the man was about to pick up a scarf, the magician appeared and said, "There you are! You need to be taught a lesson." Saying this, he held out his wand and cried, "Hocus pocus" and the man turned into a thorn bush.

26 What's in a Name?

Duncan Disorderly hated his name. His friends teased him and no matter where he went people always made fun of him. He asked his parents to change it, but they would always say, "What's in a name?" Now an Easter party was organised in his school and their school principal specially invited Mickey Mouse and Donald Duck from Disneyland to come and entertain the children. They had got lots of gifts, but there was one special gift, which would be given after a lottery. Everybody in the class said their names clear and loud. "Hey you," called Donald, "What's your name?" pointing to Duncan. "Duncan Disorderly!" mocked his classmates. "Let's give the gift to Duncan," said Mickey. "After all what's in a name. Though we have names like Mickey Mouse and Donald Duck, the world loves us." From that day nobody ever teased him again.

27 High and Lifted Up

Tommy was lying sick in his bed watching the stream of vehicles from the window. Suddenly a wind swept across. Leaves fell from the trees and twirled down the road. Tommy's eyes lit up as he watched the leaves dancing and chasing one another. "Only if I could be as free as those leaves!" sighed Tommy. He shut his eyes and suddenly found himself among those carefree leaves. Swirling up, gliding down, resting a while on roofs, then leaping back on the road. Just then a strong wind blew again and swept Tommy away towards the garbage dump. The other leaves cried, "Tommy, don't go!" Tommy woke up with a start. It was his mother crying, "Tommy, wake up." "Mother, I want to play like those leaves," cried Tommy. "But you need to take your medicines and get well first!" Soon, Tommy was fit again and was back in the fields, free as those leaves.

28 Pigs Aplenty

Pedro's bakery was stuffed with the tastiest cakes, crunchiest cookies, and the most delicious puddings. One night when Pedro went to his shop he stumbled into something. A pig! And soon he saw, not one, not two, but hundred pigs! There were pigs of different colours and sizes. Some were Chinese, some African while others were from Europe. "Get out, you slimy creatures!" he screamed. But Pedro's command fell on deaf ears, because the pigs were too busy relishing the cakes and cookies! Pedro thought of a brilliant idea. He got a broom and shouted, "If you don't clean the shop after you've finished eating, I will not allow you to enter this shop ever!" And that did the trick! Because pigs never clean, they only dirty, they rushed out of the shop and never came back!

29 Follow the Leader

Chimpoo and his dog Sheru were playing with a balloon. Suddenly there was a strong wind and little Chimpoo was lifted in the air along with the balloon. "Help! Help!" cried Chimpoo. Sheru jumped and tried to pull down Chimpoo, but he too was pulled up. "MEOW," said Lucy the cat and tried to bring down Chimpoo. But poor Lucy found herself being carried up in the air as she clung to Sheru. Cheeku the mouse rushed to help and was carried away too. A bird spotted this strange sight and pecked the balloon. BLAST! There was a loud noise as the balloon burst and Chimpoo and the animals came tumbling down on each other.

30 Paul's Tummy Ache

Little Paul was having a terrible tummy ache. "What did you eat, Son?" asked Mummy. "I couldn't sleep at all last night. My tummy is paining so much!" wailed Paul. "It seems something you ate hasn't agreed with your tummy," said Mummy. "I just ate a slice of pizza and went to sleep," said Paul innocently. Mummy shook her head quietly. She didn't know whether to believe him or not. "We'll take you to the doctor in sometime," said Daddy. After a while, when Mummy went to Paul's room, the dustbin by the door caught her attention. It was full of tiny colourful wrappers. Alas! They were candy wrappers! No wonder Paul's tummy was paining!

Contents

The Story of the Month: Margery's Garden

The Story of the Month

Margery's Garden

01 *Margery's Garden*

Margery had always lived in the city, where gardens were far and few. She longed to stay in a house with a huge garden. One day, Daddy came home and announced, "I am being transferred to a new place. We will have to move soon." "Where will we live now?" asked Margery. "Well, it's away from the city. It's a place which has a lot of greenery," replied Daddy. "Does that mean I can at last have a garden?" she asked. "We'll see," said Daddy.

When Margery arrived at the new place she was amazed. Roads were lined with trees, children's parks were well kept and every house had a garden! "Oh, I can't wait to start my garden!" thought Margery.

Soon they settled down in their new home. Margery made new friends at school but her best friend was Joe the gardener! She followed him like a shadow during all her free time. When the gardener drove the sharp end of the plough into the soil and his horse dragged it along a straight line, Margery was right there watching. She was fascinated to see the dark earth and green grass come rolling up in small waves. "Why do you have to dig the earth so much?" Margery wanted to know. Her father explained that the land had been unused for a long time and it, therefore, needed some scrambling. The next day, Joe arrived

with seeds of different shapes and sizes, some tiny plants and a package of corn. But what caught Margery's attention were the little round seeds, which looked like tiny beads. "Why are you planting beads?" she asked the gardener. "They are not beads but lettuce seeds," laughed Joe. To Margery it did not seem possible that green lettuce leaves could come from those.

"So Margery, how do you want your garden to be laid?" asked Joe. "You can put those tree saplings on the fringes, while the flowers and vegetables can grow inside," explained Margery. Holes were dug, and little pathways with stones and pebbles were laid. Margery watched Joe collect a handful of seeds and then with a gentle throwing motion let them fall out of his hand like a shower. But her favourite part of the garden was where all the colourful flower plants were being planted. Margery saw her father digging little holes with his finger and making shallow ditches. He then scattered some very small seeds lightly on the ground. In little square patches all round the garden, were planted blue bachelor's buttons, yellow marigolds, tall larkspur, multi-coloured asters, zinnias and lovely roses. Margery's father pointed out that all these lovely flowers used to grow in his grandmother's garden. "And if you don't know what they look like, you can find out next summer when they are in full bloom. It takes a lot of hard work to make a garden," he said. Margery wondered, "When will I get to see flowers...I will look after my garden carefully, Daddy."

Then one fine morning, Margery was pottering in her garden. She found many tiny buds in the flowerbed. "Mummy, Daddy, come look!" she cried. Her parents came rushing. "And the vegetables have appeared too," exclaimed her mother. Margery was very happy. She went running to all her neighbours and friends with the news of her garden. At last her dream had been fulfilled!

02 Grandfather Frog

Farmer Brown's son was a naughty boy. Grandfather Frog, who lived in the village pool was very angry with him. The boy had once hurled a stone at him and crippled his left leg and Grandfather Frog was waiting to seek his revenge.

One day, the boy sat on the edge of the pool waiting to catch fish. Grandfather Frog was alarmed. He quickly informed his fish friends how the evil boy was waiting to hook them. They quickly thought of a plan. The fish gathered around the hook and pulled it hard. Feeling the great tug, Farmer Brown's son thought it was a big fish. He became very excited and pulled the rod with great force. As per the plan the fishes let go the hook and the boy fell into the pool with a big slash! When he came out of the pool he was wet and covered with slime and weed. Grandfather Frog was watching the fun from the bank and he leaped with joy!

03 Ted Goes to School

It was Ted's first day at school and he just didn't want to go! "School is fun Ted," said his mother. "You'll make so many friends!" explained his father. His parents dropped him at the gate where Mrs. Pumpkins, Ted's new class teacher was waiting for all the new children. Mrs. Pumpkins was a kind-hearted woman. "Why are you crying, Son?" she asked. "I don't know anybody here!" wailed Ted.

Mrs. Pumpkins took Ted inside and made him sit next to Mop, a fat little boy who was busy modelling toys with clay. Ted was fascinated to see small lumps take shape. He picked up a few lumps himself and made a teddy bear! In the afternoon Mrs. Pumpkins read out beautiful stories and Ted played with all the little boys and girls. Soon it was time to go home. "So how was school?" asked Ted's parents when he reached home. "Oh, I love school and can't wait to go back tomorrow!" replied Ted.

04 The Star Dollars

A poor little girl had no room to stay in and nothing more to eat except for a piece of bread and a ragged shawl to beat the cold. One day she met an old man begging for alms. He cried, "I am very hungry. Please give me some bread!" The little girl immediately gave her bread and walked ahead. She then saw a young boy, shivering in the cold. "Could you give me something to keep me warm?" he asked. The little girl had no choice but to give her ragged shawl. At night she looked up at the star spangled sky and prayed to God to give her some shelter and food. When she opened her eyes she found star dollars, shining bright on the ground and heard a voice say, "This is your reward for doing good to others."

05 Why the Morning Glory Climbs

Morning Glories are beautiful fragrant flowers, which bloom in the morning to welcome the sun, but shut their heart-shaped petals by afternoon. It was not always the speedy climber that it is now. The flower used to lie flat on the ground and never climb up. Long ago, above her on a tree branch lived a baby wren with her mother. Her wings were broken and she could not fly. So every evening, her mother told her stories about what she saw in the world, especially stories about the beautiful Morning Glory. "There are beautiful flowers all around here, but the Morning Glory is the freshest of them all!" she told the baby wren. "How I wish I could see the flower!" cried the baby wren. The Morning Glory heard this and felt very proud, but her heart wept at the same time for the crippled baby bird. That night she decided to climb up. She struggled hard and little by little she entwined herself around the thick bark. Then holding tightly onto it, she inched up. At last in the wee hours she reached right up to where the wren's nest was and put her face on its edges. When the sun's rays trickled down through the leaves, the baby wren opened her eyes. The morning glory unfurled her petals to greet her. The baby wren jumped with joy and the beautiful flower promised to greet her and the world every morning.

06 Precious Grass

One day Brigid and Teresa, the two sisters went to the market to shop for vegetables. Each sister had a bag in her hand, which became quite heavy after shopping. On their way back home, Brigid kept complaining about how heavy her bag weighed, "How come you are smiling, Teresa, isn't your bag weighty, as well?" "No, it isn't!" replied Teresa. "I have sprinkled some precious grass on it and therefore, I don't feel the load so much!" "Tell me about that precious grass!" asked Brigid excitedly. "This precious grass which lightens all load is called patience. Brigid, you must remember that in life we have to face many hardships, but we cannot always complain. So we need to be patient and smile through times of difficulty!" Suddenly what Teresa said made a lot of sense to Brigid, and her bag felt light too!

07 The Miser

Long ago there lived a sage who was very stingy. People in his village were shocked to see a sage so mean!

One day he received a handful of rice as alms. After eating some, he kept the rest in a pot and hung it on the ceiling. While admiring the pot of rice, the man became lost in his dreams. He imagined that he would sell the rice to the villagers and with the money he gets he would purchase some cows. After having bred some more cows he would sell them in the market and get richer. On getting richer he would marry a rich man's daughter, but when she doesn't listen to him he would kick her as a punishment. In his excitement he kicked the pot and it broke.

08 The Strange Bird

Allan, Peter and Billy loved to roam in the woods. As they came in the middle of the forest, Billy shouted, "Hey! Look!" "What a strange creature," exclaimed Allan. They had never seen such a creature before. "Run, brother, run," came Peter's frightened voice.

Just as they were about to run the creature came near. "Don't run away. You have not seen me before, as I have come from far away," it said. It was a strange bird, very large and heavy with white feathers. The children looked tiny in front of it. "I miss my family in this new land. Will you all be my friends?" asked the bird.

The boys looked at each other. "Yes, why not?" The bird was happy. "Let's go for a joy ride," they shouted. The boys sat on the bird's back and flew above the forest. The bird too was happy to hear the excited chatter of its new friends and was never lonely again.

09 Susan's Dream

Susan often dreamt of visiting the land of chocolates. One night Susan woke up and found herself standing beside a chocolate fountain. "Wow! It looks so creamy and delicious," thought Susan and licked her lips. Susan looked around and saw chocolates hanging from trees, chocolate stones, chocolate houses and chocolate rivers. She found it difficult to believe her eyes and walked towards one of the chocolate houses. As the door of the house opened, she saw a beautiful maiden sitting at a table made of chocolate. "Come in, Susan," said the maiden with a smile. "Who are you?" asked Susan. "I'm the chocolate fairy. Eat as much chocolate as you want and I'll take you back home," said the fairy. Susan was very excited. She sat on a chair and started enjoying the different chocolates.

10 Fun in the Deep Blue Sea

Jenny loved fishes and she read a lot about them. When her father asked her why she loved them Jenny said, "You see, Papa, fish have a great variety. Some have a single colour, some have two colours and some are striped in yellow and blue, some are purple, orange and green. Some are too tiny, some are a little bigger and others really big. Some fish fly and some jump and frolic about and some just remain still. Did you know that some fish hide, some disappear at the blink of an eye while others sleep in the ocean and there are those which look like fishes but are not." "Jenny, I am impressed with your knowledge about the thing you love. I think you deserve a prize!" He took her to the pet shop and got her an aquarium. "Oh, thank you, Papa. You are the best!" exclaimed Jenny delightedly.

11 A Caterpillar's Voice

A caterpillar quietly sneaked into the hare's house when the latter was away. When the hare returned and found footmarks of another creature, he asked, "Who is inside?" The caterpillar replied, "I'm the one who tramples elephants and rhinos to dust!" The hare was frightened and rushed to the jackal for help. However, the jackal was also terrified when he heard the same answer. The leopard and the elephant did not dare to face the strange and scary animal inside the hare's house. Finally a frog was asked to help. The frog said in answer to the caterpillar, "I'm the one who crushes those who crush elephants and rhinos." Now the caterpillar was scared. He popped out from the hare's house and ran away. Everyone was astonished to see that a caterpillar was trying to scare them all this while and they laughed aloud.

12 The Soup

Tracy was tired of having the bland soup her mother made every day. "I'll not have soup anymore," Tracy said angrily. "I'll serve you better soup in the evening, but for now come and help me dig out potatoes from the garden," replied her mother. Tracy worked with her mother in the garden till sunset and returned home with a sack of potatoes. "Mother, I'm hungry. Get me some soup," said Tracy. This time she loved the soup and took a second helping too. Afterwards, when she asked her mother what special soup this was, her mother replied, "I gave you the same soup I had made in the morning, but you liked it now because you were tired and hungry after working the whole afternoon. It didn't matter whether the soup was tasty or not."

13 Mr. Tickles' Pink Pen

Mr. Tickles had a fine pink pen. It wrote very well and Mr. Tickles loved it. But Mr.Tickles was very forgetful and was always losing it. Sometimes it was found in the dresser, sometimes on the dinner table and at other times lying under the bed. "Why don't you keep your pen behind your ear," said Mrs. Tickles. Mr. Tickles promptly pushed the pen behind his ears. Mrs. Tickles had some urgent work and had to leave. She said to Mr. Tickles, "Will you please write a note to the sweeper and ask him to clean the chimney." When the sweeper arrived, Mr. Tickles jogged his brains trying to remember what Mrs.Tickles had asked him to do. "Umm now I remember, clean the chimney, she had said!" he said excitedly. He went to his desk, took out a writing pad and looked for his pen. As always he had forgotten where he had kept it! He looked everywhere but couldn't find the pen. He came out and said to the sweeper that he had lost his pen. "But it's behind your ear," replied the sweeper. "Oh dear, how forgetful I am," said Mr. Tickles.

14 The Short Tree

A short tree was sad because she could not grow. All the other trees around her were tall and had beautiful visitors like, chirpy sparrows and fuzzy squirrels. The short tree longed for a friend. One day, she heard a woodpecker singing in its croaky voice. The tree yelled, "Will you stop singing?" The woodpecker was shocked! "I am a lonely woodpecker and I thought if I entertain people with my songs they would befriend me." The short tree felt sorry, "Will you be my friend?" she asked. "Sure!" said the woodpecker, "But you have to let me stay on your short branch." "And you have to stop singing," said the short tree. The two became great friends and lived happily ever after.

15 The Sandy Rabbits

Mr. and Mrs. Sandy Rabbit lived with their family near the sea. Since they had lived there for many years, the hole had become old and damp so they thought of exchanging it with one that was a little further away from the sea.

Mrs. Sandy Rabbit's friend, Mrs. Eider Duck agreed to buy the hole. In return she gave Sandy two bags of downs. When Mrs. Rabbit told Mr. Sandy Rabbit about the deal, he was not at all happy. "What have you done? Now where will we sleep in the winter? We have no home," he said angrily. "Don't worry, I have an idea," said Mrs. Rabbit. The next morning, she started joining and filling the eiderdowns with bits of fluff that had come out of her bunnies bodies.

She made lots of eiderdowns and so her family were nice and cosy in the winter.

16 The Green Boat

The little green boat stood at the jetty looking at all the boats in the sea. "Oh, I wish I was big and strong like them," thought the little boat. "I don't get a chance to go farther into the sea. All I do is ferry people and goods from the big boats to the jetty and back," said the boat and sighed. The other small boats were happily bubbling in the water but the green boat was quite sad. Just then some children came along and started climbing all over the boat. It seemed they were coming to the jetty for the first time. "Oh look, such a beautiful boat," said one of them and the little boat felt better. "We can play here and come for a picnic whenever we want," said someone else. The green boat beamed with delight. So once every two weeks, the children come and spend some time in the green boat and laugh and play together. The little boat waits for them and enjoys having them around too.

17 How the Toad Got Its Skin

All the birds in the jungle were very excited about the party in the sky. The animals were upset and jealous, as they could not fly up to the sky. But the toad had thought of a plan to join the sky party.

When the birds were about to leave, the toad sneaked into the vulture's guitar and hid there. The birds arrived for the party and were both surprised and angry to see the toad!

When the party was over, the toad again quietly hopped inside the vulture's guitar. But this time, the vulture felt that his guitar had become heavier and shook it. Down went the toad falling to the earth and broke into pieces. Later, the vulture took pity on the toad and stitched up its body into one piece. Even today, one can see where the toad's body was mended by a thread and needle.

18 Larian the Lemur

In a faraway forest there lived a little lemur called Larian. Mother Lucy felt proud of Larian as he jumped high from one tree to another. One day, Larian jumped to a branch very high from the ground. The next moment Mother Lucy heard a loud thud. Larian had fallen on the ground and hurt himself. Lucy took Larian to a doctor and soon he was his old self again. A few days later, Lucy and Larian were walking in the forest when they saw a young lemur lying all alone and crying. Larian rushed to the Lemur's help and kissed him. Lucy picked up the Lemur and hugged him and said, "Oh you poor little fellow, come, we'll take you home. From now, you will stay with us. We'll call you Victor." The little lemur wiped his tears and smiled at his new family. He jumped on Larian's back and was happy again.

19 The Wise Judge

Once upon a time the people of a village decided to hold a ceremony to judge who had the best-looking child. A judge was voted and given the task of choosing the right candidate. The parents with the best looking child would be rewarded. So one by one, all the parents entered the hall with their children. A merchant who had come with his two baby boys said to the goldsmith, "Aren't my babies the prettiest of all?" "Well, you should wait and watch," said the goldsmith who was holding his beautiful daughter. Everyone lovingly showed their children to each other and waited for the competition to start. When the judge came on the stage and saw the proud parents waiting for his decision, he smiled and said, "For all parents, their children are the most beautiful and the best. So how do you expect me to choose one and declare him the winner." Everyone clapped at this and cheered for the wise judge.

20 Kelly and Melly

Two deer named Kelly and Melly were cousins. They would always be fighting over a small berry shrub, which had very delicious berries. The whole day, the two would sit on either side of the plant to keep guard lest the other gobbled up the berries. One day, Kelly threatened Melly, "If you don't leave this place, I'll bite your ears off." "And I'll bite your nose," snarled Melly. And they got into a fight, rolling over each other and trying to grab the plant. In the process, the shrub was uprooted. When they saw the shrub lying on the ground they gave up their fight. They realised how foolish they had been when they saw a smaller deer gobbling away the last remains of the plant. They decided to be friends and share their food from then on.

21 Who Has the Longest Tail

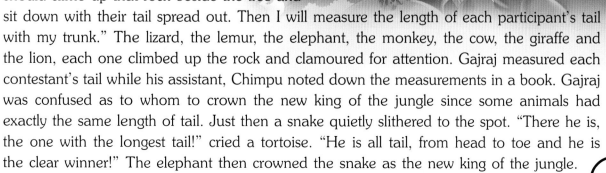

The animals in the jungle of Madhuban decided that the one with the longest tail would be made the king of the jungle. On the night of full moon, all the animals arrived one by one with their fashionably decorated tails, each confident that it would be the winner. Gajraj, the elephant announced, "Friends, when I raise my trunk and trumpet, all the contestants should climb up that rock beside the tree and sit down with their tail spread out. Then I will measure the length of each participant's tail with my trunk." The lizard, the lemur, the elephant, the monkey, the cow, the giraffe and the lion, each one climbed up the rock and clamoured for attention. Gajraj measured each contestant's tail while his assistant, Chimpu noted down the measurements in a book. Gajraj was confused as to whom to crown the new king of the jungle since some animals had exactly the same length of tail. Just then a snake quietly slithered to the spot. "There he is, the one with the longest tail!" cried a tortoise. "He is all tail, from head to toe and he is the clear winner!" The elephant then crowned the snake as the new king of the jungle.

22 Bug Beard

Mr. Woodcutter saw a sight that made him shudder. In front of him stood a very untidy man with a long beard. It had bugs running up and down it. The man was dancing to a strange song:

"Bug-da waddily, uggidy-wuggidy
Bug-da buggidy, buggidy ba!
Bug-da waddily, uggidly sluggidy
Bug-da buggidy, buggidy ba!"

Mr. Woodcutter laughed uproariously. He took the man home and asked him to meet his wife. Mr. and Mrs. Woodcutter scrubbed and scrubbed the man in a tub and shaved his buggy beard. The strange man protested but the Woodcutters held him tight. The next day, when he returned to the forest, Mr. Woodcutter was amazed to see that the forest was dying. He was puzzled at first and then a thought occurred to him. He let the man re-grow his beard, grubby and buggy. And the forest was again the same as before. The grubby, buggy man sang and danced as strangely as ever and disappeared into the forest.

23 The Rainbow's Pot of Gold

One fine morning the colourful rainbow shone bright in the sky. "Mother!" asked little Maggie excitedly, "Is it true that when the rainbow shines, a pot of gold showers down on the earth and only children receive it?" "Yes, it is true Maggie," said her mother, "but only those children who are good and not mean to others can see the gold." So Maggie decided to be a good girl and soon she received a lot of praises from her friends and relatives. "Maggie is such a lovely child!" they said. One day Maggie said to her mother, "Mother, I know what the pot of gold is!" "And what is it, Maggie?" asked her mother. "The love and praises of people," she answered. "Well spoken my child, no treasure is more valuable in the world than the love of people!" said her mother.

24   The Pink Handkerchief

One day, Mrs. Chloe was walking along the road and dropped her handkerchief. The pink handkerchief lay on the road and cried, "Oh, someone please pick me up before a lorry runs over me." Just then, a little girl was passing by and saw the little handkerchief. "Hey, that's so pretty," said she and picked it up. She put in the basket of her bicycle and then forgot all about it. When she reached home, her cat jumped into the basket and threw the handkerchief away. The handkerchief lay near the shed and waited for someone to come by. After a while, it began to rain and the little handkerchief got wet. Next morning, someone came with a broom and brushed the handkerchief away with all the dust and dirt. The pink handkerchief lay by the side of the road almost sure that it will stay there forever to rot. But guess who came along. Mrs. Chloe was passing by and felt a stone in one of her shoes. As she bent down to remove it, she saw her pink handkerchief on the ground. "Here you are!" she said, "We'll give you a good wash when we get home," and put it in her pocket.

25   Jumpy Makes Friends

Jumpy Jackal was the forest postman. Everyday he walked long distances through the forest to deliver letters to all the animals. One day, Jumpy was resting on a log and having tea after a hard day's work. A robin flew upto him and said, "Postman, can I help you?" Jumpy smiled and gave a small bite of his bun to the robin and said, "You're too tiny to be a postman." The robin flew off and soon returned with a few friends. They started taking out the letters from Jumpy's sack and soon gathered the letters together. The smaller birds took the mail and the bigger birds got hold of the parcels. Jumpy was amazed. His workload had become lighter now. Everyday the birds would come to Jumpy and help him deliver the mail. And Jumpy would give them buns in return.

26 Farmer Bob Has a Problem

Farmer Bob was very happy with the animals in his farm, until one day when he faced a strange problem. His cows had learnt to type on a typewriter that they had found in the barn. This was the strangest news the neighbourhood had ever heard and people from neighbouring villages crowded around his farm to catch a glimpse of the amazing animals.

All day Farmer Bob could hear, click! clack! and moo! click! clack! moo! clickety, clack, moo. At first he couldn't believe his ears. "Is that a typing sound that I hear?" he said to his wife as they passed by the shed. He had a look inside and saw the most unusual sight he'd ever seen- the cows were busy typing!

He was further shocked when a little later he saw a paper lying outside the shed. It was a note. The note said:

Dear Farmer Bob, it is very cold in the barn. We need electric blankets and heaters to keep our sheds warm. Yours sincerely, the Cows.

Farmer Bob was very angry now. "You are cows! I will not give you any electric blanket and neither any heater!" The cows then typed another note: We will not give you milk. Even the hens want electric blankets and heaters otherwise, they will not give you any eggs.

Now the farmer was in a fix for he did not know how to appease the animals. Then suddenly a bright idea dawned on him. He went to the shed and announced, "I will give you electric blankets and heaters if you throw away that old typewriter." The cows agreed to this deal and were happy with their new blankets and heaters.

Was Farmer Bob a happy man now? Well, not really.

The next morning he found another note. It said: The pool is very boring. Could you please build a springboard in the pool? Yours sincerely, the Ducks

Now, Farmer Bob's ducks had learnt to type. Poor Farmer Bob, he spent his days and nights thinking hard how to get rid of the typewriters!

27 Flip the Flea

Flip the flea was tired of living in a crowd. Everytime he tried to leap, he would bump into his many uncles and jumpy aunts. "There is no peace here!" said Flip while he packed his bags to leave.

He jumped off Brownie the dog that had been Flip's home until now.

Flip landed on an ant but he was too busy to talk! Flip leapt into the air and landed on a bee who chased him away with his sting. Flip then went to Pixie the kitty for a place to stay. Pixie always kept herself clean by licking her fur. Flip was always wet because of this!

Finally, Flip went back to Brownie. He was now happy with his own family of noisy cousins and uncles. "Home sweet home," thought Flip while he leapt into the air and banged into his brother Flop.

28 Twelve Men of Gotham

Twelve fishermen lived in a place called Gotham. One day, they went fishing and after spending the whole day at sea, they decided it was time to return home. "Let us count ourselves to make sure no one has drowned," said one. He counted all and found only eleven men. Then another man counted all of them and found only eleven again. No one counted himself.

Just then another fisherman passed by. "Brother, will you please help us find our twelfth man? One of us has drowned in the sea," they asked. The man counted them in his mind and found that these foolish men were not counting themselves! "What will you give me if I find your twelfth man?" "We will give you all our fish!" cried the men. The clever man quickly counted twelve men and walked away with all the fish!

29 Billy Learns to Fly

On a very windy day, Billy asked his mother, "Mom, may I go outside?" "Be careful, it's very windy today," said his mother. Billy ran out excitedly. Outside leaves of all colours swayed and flew in all directions and chased each other.

Billy watched in fascination. "How I wish I was also a leaf and was as free as them," he longed. Suddenly a maple leaf touched Billy's side and he found himself lifted up with the leaf. "I am a leaf, I am a leaf, I can't believe it," exclaimed Billy as they swirled round and round. Billy was thoroughly enjoying himself seeing the spectacular view all around. "This is so much fun," he cried. Suddenly, Billy heard his mom shout, "Billy, get up! You'll be late for school." Billy opened his eyes and realised that he had been dreaming all along. "Maybe I'll fly some other day," he thought and ran to get ready for school.

30 Monster under My Bed!

Little Kate tucked herself into bed and was about to drift into sleep when she heard a loud noise. THUMP! THUMP! Kate was petrified and she called out to her grandmother, "Grandma! There is a monster under my bed!" "That is just your naughty little heart, dearie," said Grandma.

Kate tried to go back to sleep and just then, she heard THUMP! THUMP! SCRITCH! SCRITCH! "Grandma!" she cried. "The monster is scratching his claws on the floor! Please save me!" "There is no monster, Katie!" said Grandma. "It is just your toes rubbing on the quilt!" When Katie tried to sleep once again, she felt something wet on her face! With a lot of courage, she opened her eyes to see the monster. "Grandma!" cried out Katie, "this is no monster! It's a sweet little puppy!" Katie and the puppy snuggled and slept soundly.

31 A Christmas Star

Every year for a week before Christmas, Mother Moon gathered the little stars and told them the story about the Christmas Star—the Star of Bethlehem. The stars listened to the story attentively.

"Where is that star now?" asked one of the stars.

"It shines in men's hearts," said Mother Moon.

It was almost morning on Earth so it was the stars' time to sleep. But one golden star did not go to sleep like his friends. Instead, he stayed behind with Mother Moon and asked her, "Oh Mother Moon, how can I shine in someone's heart like the Star of Bethlehem?"

Mother Moon took the little golden star to a wide open door and said, "Go inside and there you will find someone in whose heart you'll like to stay."

The next moment, the star found himself in a shop that was filled with Christmas gifts. He was hanging on a tree with many other golden and silver stars. The little golden star was amazed seeing his new place. People were busy buying gifts for Christmas. "There's so much noise around here," thought the star. He observed all the people in the shop. The star saw a little boy with his mother. The star's heart went out to him. "I want to be with this little boy," the star wished.

"Mother, I want that little golden star for my Christmas tree," the boy said pointing to the star from heaven. The little golden star found a heart to stay in.

Contents

The Story of the Month

Hairy Henry's Holiday

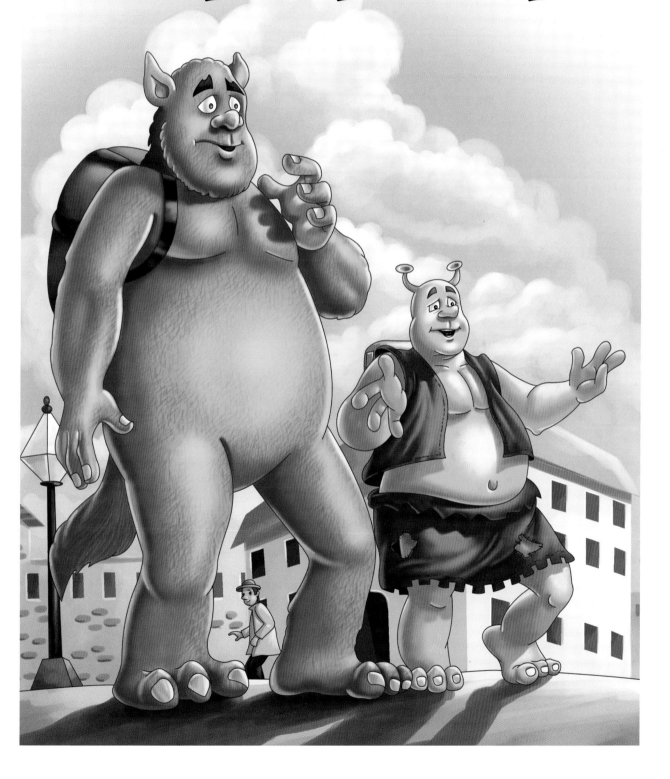

01 Hairy Henry's Holiday

Once there lived a hairy green monster named Henry. People liked Henry because he was very friendly. One day, Henry decided to go on a holiday. "I will go to visit Cousin Ben in London," he thought. Henry packed his bags and left for London on a train. When people saw a hairy green monster travelling in the train, they were terrified and stayed far away.

When he reached London, Henry walked up to the Big Ben and shouted, "Hey, Cousin Ben! Look who is here to visit you!" Ben was a clock monster who lived in the famous Clock Tower of Big Ben. "Welcome, Cousin Henry. I am so happy to see you," said Ben. Ben decided to take Henry on a sight-seeing trip all over London.

They went to a museum called Madam Tussaud's. Henry was awestruck to see wax figures of famous pop stars, footballers and kings and queens displayed there. After roaming about in the museum for a long time, Ben and Henry were very tired and sat on a bench to rest.

Some children, who were visiting the museum, saw the monsters and said, "Oh, how real those monsters look!" Just then Henry moved slightly. "The monster is alive!" they cried in fear and ran away.

Next, Ben and Henry decided to board a red double-decker bus. Now, no one has ever seen green monsters travelling in a bus. All the people in the bus screamed and got off quickly. The bus took them to a fairground. "Look! Let's take a ride on that!" pointed Ben at a huge giant wheel.

"Wheeeeeee!" cried Henry in excitement. Hearing his thunderous voice, all the other people on the giant wheel nearly fell off! "I can see the river and the palace and, oh look! The people are looking so tiny!" laughed Henry.

Feeling giddy after their ride, Henry and Ben rested for some time. "Henry, you must travel by the tube," said Ben. "It is amazing to travel in an underground train!" Soon, they arrived at a big castle. But the monsters did not go inside the castle. Instead, they went to a secret place under the castle. "Where are we?" asked Henry. "We are in a dungeon," replied Ben. It was so dark and spooky that even the monsters were nervous.

After a long day, Henry and Ben went back to Ben's home in the Clock Tower. Alas, it was time for Henry to go back. They hugged each other and Henry said, "Cousin Ben, I had a splendid time with you. We will meet again soon."

Hairy Henry had had a lovely holiday, indeed!

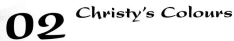

02 Christy's Colours

Christy loved colours. Every day, she took her big book and sat at a table and made a picture. Then Mummy put the picture up on the wall in Christy's room. One day, Christy decided to paint a little cottage beside a stream. She painted the roof of the cottage red, the stream a beautiful blue, the sky blue and the sun bright yellow. "Green, green," she searched for green to paint the grass. But accidentally her hand hit the blue paint bottle and some blue paint dropped on the yellow paint. And lo! It turned green. "Oh, this is magic!" exclaimed Christy in delight and she started mixing all the colours with each other. Mixing yellow and red gave her bright orange, red and white turned to pink, with red and blue she had purple. White and black gave her grey and Christy made some clouds in her picture. At the end, Christy completed her picture with lots of green grass and beautiful flowers in orange, pink and purple.

03 The Greedy Hippo

Once there lived a very greedy hippo. He was always eating and never cared whether the other animals had anything to eat or not. All he wanted was to fill his own stomach. One day, after a hearty breakfast, the hippo went to bathe in his favourite pool. But he was so fat that he got stuck in the pool! All the other animals who lived nearby rushed to pull him out, but instead of thanking them, he ran past them and ate up all their food! The animals decided to teach the hippo a lesson. One day, they baked a fish pie with soap in it and offered it to the greedy hippo. The hippo gulped it down at once without any thank-you to the others. That night he had a terrible stomachache and realised that he had been tricked. He packed his bags and left the jungle. The last they saw of him, the greedy hippo was blowing soapy bubbles!

04 The Mountain Story

Once little Timmy and his father were travelling high up the mountains. After a while, Timmy stumbled on a rock and fell down. "Aaaagh!" he cried out in pain. To his surprise, he heard a voice calling back, "Aaaagh!" Timmy called out, "Who are you?" The voice replied, "Who are you?" He said, "You are great!" The voice repeated, "You are great!" Then Timmy yelled, "You are a coward!" and the voice yelled back, "You are a coward!" Timmy was at once scared and excited. Just then, his father came to Timmy and said, "Son, that is an echo. It will repeat whatever you say. Try to say good things so that it says good things back to you. Life is like an echo. You will get what you give. Always be good and do good to others." Timmy was a smart boy and understood what his father was telling him. Do you?

05 Bensie

All day, Bensie loved to play in Mrs. J's lawn. He loved to chase butterflies with his sister, Mopsie. Today, the puppies raced about in the grassy lawn and trampled all over Mrs. J's roses. Bensie had also scattered the vegetables in the patch. Away went the cucumbers and the tomatoes! Away went the lettuce and radishes! What fun they had, until Bensie saw Mrs. J's face. She looked as though she would burst into tears! Bensie loved Mrs. J more than anyone in this world and he knew he had made her sad. Bensie was truly very sorry. But to his surprise, Mrs. J patted him and said, "I know you love to play, don't you worry about the vegetables! You are just a teeny-weeny puppy!" Bensie felt so happy. He licked her face and raced about in the lawn. Bensie was also a little worried about what Mr. J would say. Thankfully, Mr. J did not get angry either. "Who can stay mad at you?" smiled Mr. J while Bensie wagged his tail.

06 Simon and His Old Shoes

Old Simon loved his brown shoes. They were more than twenty years old. He found them so comfortable that he didn't want to give them away and buy a new pair. "Why do I need new shoes? These are better than the best!" he always said. He would wear them for special occasions too. One day, Simon received an invitation from an old friend. Simon took out his old pair of shoes and what did he see! A bird had made a nest in one of the shoes and there lay four little baby birds, sleeping peacefully. Simon frowned and looked at the birds. They were s-o-o-o small. Simon felt sorry for them. He did not want to make them homeless. So he went to the market and bought a pair of new shoes.

07 The Beautiful Fairy

A little girl named Betty lived with her mother in a small cottage. They were poor and often had to go without food. Every day, Betty had to go to the river to fetch water. One day, a beautiful fairy suddenly appeared. She was wearing a very pretty blue dress and had wings too! Betty stared at her in disbelief. The fairy asked Betty to dance with her. They both danced till evening and soon it was time for Betty to go home. The fairy appeared again the next day and then they sang and danced together. When it was time for Betty to go home, the fairy gave her a small bag and told her to look inside it when she reached home. But Betty was so curious that she opened the bag. "Oh!" she exclaimed in dismay, "there are just some dry birch leaves here." She threw some of them away. When she reached home, Betty told her mother all about the fairy. Her mother picked up the bag; it seemed heavy. Imagine her surprise when she opened it to find gold coins inside. Betty and her mother never had to go without food ever again.

08 Mitty's Wait

Mitty the puppy was bored. Midget the cat was in no mood to play. "Midget, please come out and play with me in the sun!" pleaded Mitty. "Not today, Mitty. I can't. I will just stay in this basket for a while. One of these days, I am going to give you a surprise but you must be patient for now."

Mitty wandered alone for a few days. He would follow his mistress, while she cooked and cleaned. Finally, one day, he saw Midget lying in her basket with FIVE tiny kittens! One white, two black, one grey and one with patches! Midget said, "Mitty, you have been so patient all these days. As a reward, I want you to name my five kittens!" Mitty was so happy and he sat there thinking for a while. Guess what the names were? Rolley, Polley, Dipsey, Doodle and Noodle!

09 Little Susie Becomes an Elephant

Last summer little Susie and her cousins staged an animal play at her grandfather's farmhouse. So when Mrs. Kitty announced that they would have an animal show in school, Susie jumped in excitement. "I did this before and I love being a bear." So Mrs. Kitty asked her to direct the play and guide the other children. Susie showed little Ronnie how to run like a squirrel and taught Tom how to roar like a tiger. Susie and Jill decided to become an elephant. She asked her mother, "What kind of costume shall I wear?" Mummy had a ready solution. She rummaged Daddy's old trunk and brought out a B-I-G grey coat. Jill and Susie bent down and the coat was draped over them. One of the sleeves became the trunk. The whole theatre clapped loud as the 'elephant' entered, swinging his long trunk. The play was a grand success and everyone praised Susie for her direction and acting.

10 The Skating Competition

Patrick decided to organise a skating competition on his father's birthday. All his friends loved skating and were going to participate. A day before the race, the boys went to practice and saw a young boy practising on wooden skates. He was wearing very shabby clothes. "Hello! I'm Robert. Can I participate in the competition?" said the boy to Patrick. "Ha! Ha! Look, he doesn't even have proper skates," laughed everyone except Patrick. Patrick had noticed that Robert was skating very well. He immediately offered to give Robert his skates. Robert wore Patrick's skates for the competition and skated like a professional skater. He left the others far behind and won the race. Patrick's father was very proud of his son and said, "You have given me the best birthday gift by helping that poor boy!"

11 A Box Full of Kisses

Little Maria was very excited. It was Daddy's birthday. She shook her little piggy bank. It was empty. She had spent all her money on a new doll last month. "Oh, how I wish I had some money! I could have bought something for Daddy today." Suddenly, she had a bright idea. She ran to the attic to find a big box and some wrapping paper. She chose the biggest box she could find and even managed to find some silver paper and fancy ribbons. After a while, she went to wake up Daddy. "Happy Birthday," she shouted and proudly handed Daddy her present. Daddy was amazed. He wondered what Maria could have got for him in such a big box. He unwrapped the box carefully and opened the lid. Alas! The box was empty. Daddy laughed and said, "Hmm…I knew you were up to something." "Oh Daddy," explained Maria, "Look carefully, I blew so many kisses inside the box…all for you. Sooo many," spreading her arms as wide as she could. Daddy gave Maria a big hug! "That's the best present ever!" he said.

12   The Wolf-Donkey

Sandy Rabbit hated carrots. Everyday Mama Rabbit scolded him. "Sandy, if you don't eat carrots your eyesight will become weak." But he never listened to her. Finally, Mama had an idea. She told Dum Dum Donkey, "Can you come to my burrow tonight and howl like a wolf?" Then Mama went to the squirrel and the sparrow. "Please pretend to be frightened when you hear Dum Dum snarl tonight," she told them. In the evening, Sandy hopped out of his burrow. Suddenly, he saw Dum Dum and was surprised to hear him snarl like a wolf. "Run Sandy, it's the big bad wolf," the squirrel and the sparrow screeched. "It's only Dum Dum Donkey," replied Sandy. "Sandy! Your eyesight was weak and now you can't even hear properly. Didn't you hear the wolf?" said Mama Rabbit. Sandy ate carrots without any fuss from that day onwards.

13   Little Nancy Runs Away

Little Nancy had a little baby brother, Ted. Everyone thought he was very sweet. He kept everybody so busy. One night, Granny forgot to tell Nancy a bedtime story. Mummy had promised to stitch a new skirt for Nancy's doll but she didn't get any time either. Nancy was very upset. "It seems no one loves me anymore," she thought. Next morning, Nancy slipped out of the house and went to hide in a little cave in the park nearby. When Nancy was not to be found anywhere, everyone at home was very worried. Mummy and Daddy went to look for her. Soon, they found her sitting in the corner of the cave. Mummy picked up Nancy and gave her a big hug. "Why are you hiding here?" she asked. Nancy tearfully said, "Nobody loves me. I ran away." "Oh dear," smiled Mummy, "We all love you very, very much. Ted has been crying all day because you were not home today. Come, let's go home. I've made some apple pie for you." "Wow! Yumm..." squealed Nancy and ran home.

14 Donald's Adventures

Donald was a naughty little fish who lived with his family in a big river that whooshed into the sea. One day, Donald read about Peter Pan and Neverland. "It must be on the other side of the sea," thought Donald. Next morning he decided to go to Neverland and swam towards the sea. As soon as he reached the sea, a big wave swooped him up and took him far away. "Wh-e-e-e!" cried little Donald in excitement. Deep into the sea he saw so many fish—blue ones, red ones, striped ones and dotted ones. Then suddenly he saw a shark snapping his teeth at the other fish. In his hurry to swim away from the shark, Donald didn't notice the net spread over the water and was trapped in it. The fisherman in the boat put him into a big basket with the other fish. Now, there was a tiny hole in it and Donald squeezed his way out through it. He then jumped into the river and rushed back home.

15 Down in the Ocean

A fish called Trish lived deep in the ocean. To look pretty was her only wish. Next comes Stan the grumpy old clam. Never to be made dinner was his only plan.

Then, there was Scott, the wise lobster who never got caught.

Down in the deep blue ocean lived a sponge called Mary who found the deep blue ocean scary. Not to forget Bree, the shark who longed to be free.

There goes the dolphin, Tipsy. She loved to swim and had much to see. Rusty, the jellyfish never came out of the water. So, Rusty was never dusty. But the biggest of them was Gayle, the whale, who though large was a bit frail.

But my favourite was the fat crab named John who was always singing a song. Hope you enjoyed reading about my friends down in the ocean. I'm sure you'll agree that they are wonderful.

16 Martha's Summer Vacation

Summer holidays had begun but Martha was glum. All her friends had left town and were holidaying in beautiful islands and cities of the world. "Brandy went to Paris, Susan is in Seychelles and I'm left all alone!" moaned Martha.

Martha looked so sad and lonely that her mother decided to give her a surprise. Next morning, Martha woke up to the sound of a little whimper. "Oh, what's this?" she thought as she saw a little basket near her bed. Guess what! A little pup was peeping out from the basket. It was a young German Shepherd. "Martha, here's your new friend!" said her mother. Martha jumped out of bed in excitement. She cuddled the little pup and said, "Hey, I'm going to call you Brownie." Martha was not lonely anymore. She gave Brownie a bath, took care of her, played with her and took her for long walks every day.

17 Susan and Her Shoes

Susan had a pair of red shoes. They were very pretty but when she walked, they made a funny squeaky sound. Once she wore them to a birthday party and they squeaked, "Squeak! Squeak! Squeak!" All the children thought there was a mouse in the room and were scared. At home, her mother didn't like the sound either. One day she told Susan, "Honey, when you wear these shoes, I feel that the room is full of mice. "Ughhhh!" Susan was every upset. Nobody liked her shoes. She decided to throw them in the dustbin in the garden. She decided to wear them for the last time and walked to the garden. As usual, the shoes went, "Squeak! Squeak! Squeak!" Suddenly she heard a loud "Meow!" and a cat jumped on her feet. The cat must have thought there's a mouse around. And lo! Strangely, the shoes stopped squeaking since then and Susan did not have to throw them away. She still wears them to all the parties.

18 Bunty Rabbit Runs a Race

One day Bunty Rabbit asked his mother, "Mama, why did great-great-great-grandfather lose the race against the tortoise? You know, everyone laughed at me when the teacher told us the story." "Great-great-great-grandfather was very proud. That's why he lost the race," said Mama Rabbit.

"But I'll race with Dozy Tortoise and defeat him. I'll show him that only speed and swiftness win races." Mama Rabbit tried to stop her son from doing anything foolish but he did not listen and went straight to Dozy Tortoise who was sleeping under a tree. "Dozy, I challenge you to a race tomorrow. We'll start from here and finish the race at the bridge," announced Bunty.

The next morning, the race began. Slimy Frog was the umpire. But lo! To everyone's great wonder, once again, Dozy Tortoise was the winner! He had put on roller skates!

19 Entry to Heaven

A poor cobbler arrived near the gates of Heaven. At the same time there was a rich merchant who was also waiting to get into heaven. A guard came with the key to heaven. He took the rich merchant inside but didn't see the poor cobbler. The poor man was left standing outside. He heard music and rejoicing inside for the rich man. The cobbler had expected the same welcome on entering heaven. Finally, the angels welcomed the cobbler too and showered affection on him but no one sang for him. So, he asked the angels why there should be partiality in heaven. The guard replied that he was equally dear to God and would enjoy every heavenly delight like the others. But poor people like him came to heaven every day whereas rich men came very rarely.

20 The Bandaged Bicycle

Dr. Tabby was in his chamber when the telephone rang. It was Mrs. Herring. "Doctor, please come quickly. Mr. Herring has fallen off a ladder," she sounded worried. Dr. Tabby immediately rushed off on his bicycle. Nurse Betty followed him. They found Mr. Herring sitting on the ground in front of his house. Some nails were strewn on the ground near him. "I was 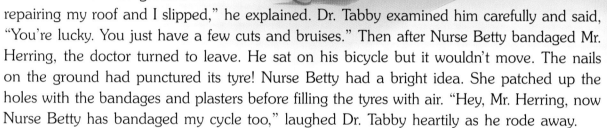 repairing my roof and I slipped," he explained. Dr. Tabby examined him carefully and said, "You're lucky. You just have a few cuts and bruises." Then after Nurse Betty bandaged Mr. Herring, the doctor turned to leave. He sat on his bicycle but it wouldn't move. The nails on the ground had punctured its tyre! Nurse Betty had a bright idea. She patched up the holes with the bandages and plasters before filling the tyres with air. "Hey, Mr. Herring, now Nurse Betty has bandaged my cycle too," laughed Dr. Tabby heartily as he rode away.

21 Twenty Dollars

A famous speaker was coming to town that day. Matt's parents had bought a ticket for Matt too, but he was not interested. He reluctantly agreed to go with his parents to attend the programme. Everyone applauded when the speaker came on the stage. He held a $50 note and asked everyone, "Who wants this?" At once many hands went up. Then to everyone's surprise, the speaker crumpled the note and again asked the  same question. And yet again as many hands were raised up. "Now, what if I do this?" Then the speaker began to grind the note under his shoe. Still there were hands in the air. "My friends, I have something valuable to tell you," said the speaker. "We are also like the $50 note. Many times we too are crushed down in life by circumstances. But, our value is not lost to those who love us. You still wanted the $50 because even though it was crushed and crumpled, it had not lost its worth. Each one of you is special." That evening, Matt said to his parents, "I'm glad I went for that talk. I'll tell my friends what I have learnt."

22 Bunny and the Wild Sheep

Bunny was a good-hearted, gentle and sensitive rabbit. One day, as he was basking in the sun his friend Maddy, a big brown dog approached him. "Bunny," said Maddy, "I am looking for a caretaker for my sheep and I think you would be perfect." Bunny soon realised that the sheep were very disobedient and ill-mannered. They did exactly what Bunny told them not to do. Bunny was so vexed that he thought, "I should give up the work." But before he could make up his mind, he heard the sheep bleating frantically. A deadly pack of wolves had trapped them and they were helplessly crying. Gentle Bunny diverted the wolves' attention and freed the sheep. The sheep felt ashamed of their behaviour and promised, "We will never play pranks on you again. Please, forgive us!"

23 Mrs. Gibbins' New Hat

Mrs. Gibbins loved wearing hats. One day, she made a brown hat. She decorated it with pink beads and green ribbons. Then she found some pretty feathers and put them on the crown. She also managed to find some fine lace and added it to her hat. When it was ready, she stood back and looked at it. "Now, doesn't that look good?" she said to herself. "I'm going to go to the grocer's and I'll wear you," she said to the hat. Mrs. Gibbins put on her new hat and walked down the street. She went to the grocery and the Laundromat. When she returned home, she took her hat off. What a surprise she got! A little sparrow had made a nest and even laid an egg! There she sat, perched on Mrs. Gibbins' hat! Mrs. Gibbins put the hat away and waited for the egg to hatch. A few days later, a little chick sat on Mrs. Gibbins' hat and can still be seen on her window sill even today.

24 The Blind Men and the Elephant

Four blind men went to a zoo. The zoo elephants gave them a really tough time. Alas! The zookeeper had forgotten to lock the gate of the elephants' cage. The elephants slipped out and decided to go for a walk.

When the elephants crossed the four blind men, one of the men

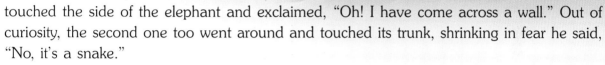

touched the side of the elephant and exclaimed, "Oh! I have come across a wall." Out of curiosity, the second one too went around and touched its trunk, shrinking in fear he said, "No, it's a snake."

The other two also went one by one and came to different conclusions of it being a rope, a sword and a tree trunk.

At last they went to the zookeeper who told them, "It was neither a rope nor a tree trunk but a big elephant." They then realised that it is wrong to make hasty decisions.

25 Bath Time

Little Kenny was two years old. He loved having a bath. Every morning, Mummy would call Kenny when it was time for his bath. "Kenny, the water's ready," said Mummy one morning. Kenny rushed to the bathroom. He picked up a tube and squeezed some of it into the tub. Oooooh!! Soon the tub was full of bubbles. Kenny looked around for his toys. He

threw his boat and a little whale in the tub. Then he threw two little ducks and his red ball. "Mmm…have I forgotten something?" he wondered. Mummy was standing just behind Kenny. She laughed and gave him a little push and said, "Yes, honey, you've forgotten yourself." Kenny laughed and jumped into the tub.

26 Love and Time

Once upon a time all the feelings in the world lived together on a beautiful sunny island. They were: Happiness, Sadness, Love, Vanity, Knowledge, Anger and many others.

One day, it so happened that all the feelings came to know that the island was about to sink. Now, they all planned to leave the island as soon as possible. All of them packed their bags except for Love. "Why, Love, aren't you going to get out of this island?" asked Knowledge. "No," replied Love, "I will hold on until the last possible moment."

When the island began to sink, Love looked out for help. She saw Richness pass by on a boat. "Richness!" Love cried, "Please save me! Please give me some place in your boat!" "Sorry, Love, there is no place on my boat because of bags of gold and silver!" said Richness "Why don't you ask Saddness, all she needs is a friend to cheer her up!" she added jokingly.

Then came Sadness. "Sadness!" cried Love, "please give me some place in your boat!" "Love, I am so sad that I want to be alone!" said Sadness and rowed away. Then came Vanity. "Love! You are so wet!! I can't spoil my dainty little boat! I am sorry I can't help you!" Finally Anger, angrily said to Love, "You are a fool, you think people have all the time in the world for you. Goodbye. You can stay all alone on this island!"

Just when Love was about to give up hope, someone old got hold of her and pulled Love into a boat. They rowed away to safety. When they were on dry land, the old man walked away even before Love could thank him. Confused, Love asked Knowledge, "Who was that elder person who saved my life?" Knowledge replied, "That was Time. Only Time knows the value of Love. He knows it is the greatest emotion for its invaluable."

27 Susie and Cathy

Susie and Cathy were very good friends. One day at school, their teacher, Mrs. Brimstone, asked all the children to search for things that were hidden in the classroom. "Susie and Cathy you're going to search for ten pencils. Ruth and Ross, search for ten scales," said Mrs Brimstone. When she blew the whistle, everyone scampered all over the room but Susie and Cathy were very organised. First, Susie found two pencils under the chair. Cathy quickly found three pencils inside the cupboard. They found another two in the Grumpy Pumpkin, their favourite pencil holder. Another two, they found in Bunny Rabbit's kitty bag. Bunny Rabbit was the new toy member of the game room. But where was the last one? They searched for long but couldn't find the pencil. Then suddenly Susie noticed the "Use Me" bear and Cathy rummaged and found the pencil at last. They were the first pair to finish the search. Mrs. Brimstone was very happy and gave them a box of chocolates.

28 King No Fun and Smarty Pants

King No Fun did not like people having fun. "No one works when they have fun!" he would say. So, the king banned people from having fun. There were posters all over the kingdom that read, "No Fun!"

One day, a young knight named Sir Smarty Pants, came to the kingdom. He told the king, "I want to dance my 'smarty pants dance' in this kingdom!" The king said, "No dancing! Dancing is fun!" "You mean," said the knight, "I can't dance like this?" Saying this, Sir Smarty Pants danced the most fun dance ever! The king and all his men joined in the dance. The whole kingdom started dancing but not when they had work to do.

Now, King No Fun realised that even though people were dancing and having fun, no one stopped working. "So, fun is not so bad after all!" said King No Fun.

29 Sara's New Friends

Sara's family was new to the city. One day, Sara's neighbour, Paula invited her to her little sister's birthday party. They had a lot of fun and played games all evening. That evening, Sara was very quiet. Mummy patted her and asked, "What happened, darling? Why are you so quiet?" "Mummy, I want a little sister so that I have someone to play with," said Sara. Mummy thought for a while and said, "Well, let me see what I can do." Next morning, she took Sara to a huge white building. "Where are we, Mummy?" she asked. "This is an orphanage. Many children live here. They don't have any brothers and sisters and want someone to play with them too." Sara saw some little boys and girls and played with them. Mummy gave Sara some chocolates to give to her new friends. Soon, it was time to go home. "Thanks Mummy, I had a lovely time. Can I come here again"? "Of course," smiled Mummy, "You can come here every Sunday and get some of your toys to share with your new friends." Sara was very happy.

30 Surprise Dessert

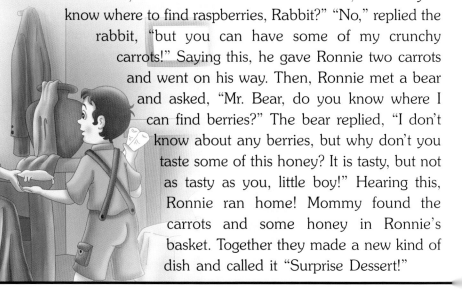

"Ronnie!" said Mommy, "I am going to make a pie for dessert. Will you pick some raspberries for me?" Ronnie was elated. He loved picking berries! So, off went Ronnie to the meadow to collect some berries. There, Ronnie saw a rabbit and asked, "Would you know where to find raspberries, Rabbit?" "No," replied the rabbit, "but you can have some of my crunchy carrots!" Saying this, he gave Ronnie two carrots and went on his way. Then, Ronnie met a bear and asked, "Mr. Bear, do you know where I can find berries?" The bear replied, "I don't know about any berries, but why don't you taste some of this honey? It is tasty, but not as tasty as you, little boy!" Hearing this, Ronnie ran home! Mommy found the carrots and some honey in Ronnie's basket. Together they made a new kind of dish and called it "Surprise Dessert!"

31 Land of the Sun

Long ago there lived two groups of people in an island known as the "Land of the Sun." One group was called the "Know-it-alls" and the other group was called "Find-it-alls." There was a thick wall separating the two areas where these people stayed.

The number of people on both sides of the wall began to grow as the years passed. There was no place for the people to stay. One day, because of all the rush and crowd, the great wall was torn down. This was the first time in many years that the people on both the sides of the wall got to see each other!

What they saw surprised the people. The Know-it-alls looked very similar to each other. They wore similar clothes. They had similar expressions on their faces and they never asked any questions. They were supposed to know everything.

The Find-it-alls on the other hand looked so different from each other. They wore different styles of clothes in different colours. While some frowned, some smiled. While some were surprised, others were happy. Every Find-it-all seemed to have a life of his own. This is because they asked questions and tried to find the answers in their different ways. There were better buildings and parks in this side of the island. The Know-it-alls now realised the importance of learning new things. From that day onwards, there was no wall in between the two groups. They all lived happily with each other ever after.

Contents

The Story of the Month: Hula's Land of Snow

The Story of the Month

Hula's Land of Snow

01 Hula's Land of Snow

It was a cozy winter evening and, Wilma and her dog, Hula, were sitting on the bed. Wilma was reading a book. The dog's picture on the book resembled Hula. Suddenly, Wilma had a bright idea. "Hula," asked Wilma, "would you like to meet your family?" Hula wagged his tail in excitement and licked Wilma's face all over.

Now, finding Hula's family was not easy. It took days to prepare for the trip. Wilma thought, "I should carry lots of woollens, eatables and bones for Hula." Wilma was sure that Hula's family lived in a very cold region because of the thick fur on Hula's body. And the picture on the book was of an area full of snow.

Wilma and Hula went towards the north. They travelled for many days and nights. As each day passed, it got colder and colder. They snuggled together at night to keep themselves warm.

The Pole Star in the sky saw Wilma and Hula and decided to help them find the way. He said, "Don't worry, dear children. I will make sure you don't get lost." The stars changed their positions but the pole star stood at the same point and guided the little travellers.

One morning, Wilma and Hula arrived at a place they saw a hut with smoke coming out of it in the distance. "Hula!" cried Wilma excitedly, "I see something moving around that heap of snow. Let's go and see what it is."

"Hurrah!" Wilma shouted in joy when she saw that all the dogs looked like Hula. "This is your family, Hula," said Wilma. Hula jumped in excitement and hugged his brothers and sisters. Just then, Wilma saw a dangerous polar bear coming towards them. She was startled and started running away in fear.

"Hula! Hula!" screamed Wilma, but Hula was too busy with her family to hear. Wilma slipped and fell on the ground. The fierce beast charged towards her. Just then, all the dogs made a circle around Wilma and forced the bear to run away.

Wilma thanked Hula's family for saving her life. After spending a few days with them, they started their journey back home. Their adventure was over and Hula wagged his tail vigorously, happier than ever.

02 Mrs. Tittlemouse and the Bumblebee

Mrs. Tittlemouse baked delicious cakes everyday. A bumblebee who lived nearby longed for the cakes. But Mrs. Tittlemouse disliked insects. If she ever spotted a spider weaving a web, she chased the spider out of her house with her broomstick. "How will I ever get to taste those those delicious cakes?" wondered the bumblebee. One day, a caterpillar happened to sit on the window sill. "How dare you come here!" shouted Mrs. Tittlemouse "Please have pity on me, I have hurt my leg!" pleaded the butterfly. Meanwhile, the bumblebee watched on anxiously from behind a tree. Mrs. Tittlemouse gently applied medicines to the caterpillar's wounds and offered some cake. "Great idea!" muttered the bumblebee. Next morning, the bumblebee buzzed near the window, complaining of a headache. Alas! Mrs. Tittlemouse saw through his plan and chased him away with her broomstick.

03 Katie and the Fairy

Katie had read many stories about Fairyland. "Please take me to Fairyland," she would often pray to God. One day, while Katie was playing in her garden, a beautiful fairy appeared. "Katie, would you like to go with me to Fairyland?" she said. "Err… I would love too. But who are you?" asked Katie. "I'm the princess of Fairyland," replied the fairy. So off they went in a flying chariot. Katie saw the most beautiful flowers she had ever seen and had the tastiest chocolate. The fairy gave Katie a beautiful dress with lots of frills and flounce and a pair of glass shoes. Suddenly Katie felt a jerk and opened her eyes. There was nobody around. But she was still wearing her beautiful dress and her glass shoes. "Oh God! I actually visited Fairyland," murmured Katie and ran inside to tell her mother.

04 Jolly Monster's Birthday

It was Jolly Monster's birthday and he had invited all his friends for a party. He knew that he would get lots of gifts but this time he was hoping for something special—a really big birthday present! In the evening when his friends arrived, someone gave him huge monster gloves, another gave him a cap. He also got a toy car and some large balloons. Jolly Monster was not very happy and anxiously waited for that special gift. Just then the lights went off and there was pindrop silence. Suddenly there was a loud cheering and the room was full of light again. "Happy birthday to you!" sang his friends and presented Jolly Monster with a huge blow up castle! "Wow! This is the best surprise ever!" laughed Jolly Monster as he bounced up and down on his blow-up castle.

05 Mr. Knowall and His Forgetfulness

Mr. Knowall never knew why he kept forgetting his glasses. His cousin Miss Forgetty, quite unlike her name never forgot anything. One day, as usual, Mr. Knowall lost his glasses. "Why can't I remember where I have kept them?" said Mr. Knowall. Miss Forgetty gave him a stern look and said, "Not again!" Just then, Mr Portly, their neighbour entered the house. "Mr. Portly, nice to see you. Come and sit with us," said Mr. Knowall and told him all about his missing glasses. "Hmmm...I think I saw something on the sofa..." said Mr. Portly scratching his head. "SOFA!" screamed Miss Forgetty. "Would you mind standing up, Mr. Portly?" Mr. Portly stood up and there were Mr. Knowall's glasses! Alas, they were broken. Miss Forgetty had a bright idea. "Next time you want to remember something," said she, "just tie a knot in your handkerchief." The plan was almost successful but there was one little problem. Mr. Knowall kept losing his handkerchief!

06 Glotty Rabbit's Day Out

Glotty was a small rabbit who lived with his mother in a cozy little burrow. Mother always chose the best carrots for Glotty. One day, before going for carrot-hunting, Mother said, "Glotty, while I am away, you must stay indoors. You are still just a baby and I don't want you to get lost!" When Mother left, Glotty ran outside. "I am not a baby! I am old enough to go out on my own. I am not scared of anyone!" Saying so, Glotty scampered into the woods. He played hide and seek in the tall grass, chased little butterflies and picked berries. "Hissss!" Suddenly, a huge snake appeared in front of him! Now, Glotty froze on the spot. Thankfully, Coco the mongoose saw what was happening. He pounced on the snake and held him tight. From that day onwards, Glotty never disobeyed his mother.

07 Haku's Power

Haku was a stonecutter who lived in Japan. One day, he saw the emperor passing by in his curtained carriage. "I want a carriage ride. If only I were the emperor!" sighed Haku. Suddenly, Haku found himself seated inside the carriage! He was the emperor now! But it was a sunny day and Haku felt stuffy inside the carriage. "The sun is so powerful that I am feeling uncomfortable! If only I were the sun!" thought Haku. Before he could blink, Haku had become the sun. Haku was happy being the sun, until a few clouds blocked him. "Dark clouds are more powerful than me! I want to be a cloud!" he thought. Haku was now a rain cloud! He started to pour immediately. One day, Haku saw a huge black boulder and thought, "It's been raining for so many days but I have not been able to move that boulder! If only I were a stonecutter!" Poof! Haku was back to his old happy self!

08   Eric the Engine

Sergy Seagull saw a huge boulder on the railway tracks. "My! My! The London train will come by in an hour or so!" thought Sergy. She knew she couldn't do anything on her own. So, Sergy flew to her friends, Jack Rabbit, Muriel Mouse and Jerome Jackal. The animals rushed to the scene and tried to move the boulder but in vain.

"We should call Eric the engine to help us!" cried Muriel. They went to Eric and told him about the huge boulder. Eric chugged to the track and tried to push the boulder, but he was only a small engine. "What do we do now?" worried Jerome. Eric had an idea. He let out a really loud whistle and called all his other engine friends. Together, they managed to push the boulder off the track. Just then, the London train sped past and it let out a long "thaaaaaaaaaaaaaank youuuuuuuuuu" whistle!

09   Red Birdie's Party

Red Birdie had just moved to Bird Land. He thought, "I shall invite everyone to a party. I will be able to make new friends then." So he flew up and down the street and dropped an envelope in every letterbox of Bird Land. Next morning, he decorated his house and baked a delicious cake and made cheese sandwiches. He waited for his guests to arrive but no one came. He flew outside and saw many birds flying up and down the street with presents in their hands.

"Do you know Red Birdie's house?" they asked him anxiously.

Red Birdie laughed when he realised that he had put the numbers on his gate upside-down. His house number was 61 but the numbers on the gate said 91. Everyone had a good laugh. They had lots of fun and Red Birdie made many friends.

10 Bobby Gets Dressed

Bobby was a good boy, but he was never ready in time for school in the morning. Everyone used to get annoyed at this. Bobby was late for school everyday.

One morning, his sister, Susie, had a great idea. She put all his clothes inside a pillowcase. "Bobby," she said. "Let's play a game. I am going to play this toy xylophone now. When the music stops, you have to take something out of the pillowcase and wear it!" Bobby loved playing games. Everytime Susie stopped the music, Bobby would take out a shirt or a sock and wear it. Now Bobby was ready for the school. Such a clever girl Susie was! Bobby was never ever late for school again!

11 Hermia the Hippo

Hermia the hippo lived in a zoo. One day, Hermia escaped from the zoo and ran away to Mike's house. Mike knew that hippos and boys couldn't stay together, so he hid Hermia in their swimming pool. Hermia stayed in the water quietly and didn't make any noise. She was quite pleased with herself. At night, Mike sneaked out food from the kitchen and Hermia gulped it all in seconds! Hippos really have a large appetite. But Mother found out about Hermia when they were playing in his room and jumping on the bed. She was shocked at the sight. "Mike! You know that hippos stay in zoos! We must take her back immediately," cried Mother. Now Mike goes to the zoo every Sunday to meet Hermia.

12 Rainforest Adventure

Nell and Rocco decided to go sailing in their new boat. They packed food and set off. Everything was going on well, until they came to the bend of the river. The engine went 'Phut! Phut!' and stopped. "Oh no!" cried Rocco. "What do we do now?" Nell was still in good spirits. "Let's start our picnic now!" he said.

They ate yummy sandwiches and drank lemonade. Nell noticed how green the riverbanks were. They were in the middle of a rainforest! Dark green creepers were on huge trees and many chirpy insects all around! Rocco loved the mangrove trees. Their roots were so big. There were merrily chattering toucans perched on trees. When the boat touched the riverbank, they got off and explored the land. They spent the day in this amazing place and repaired the boat. Nell and Rocco had so much to talk about the next day, at school!

13 Evergreen Trees

Once a little bird was flying south for the winter. On his way, he hurt his wings and couldn't fly further. He went to the birch tree. "Will you please let me stay in your branches this winter?" he asked. The birch tree refused. Then he went to the oak tree. The tree said, "I won't let you stay! What if you eat my precious acorns?" Disheartened, the little bird went to the willow tree and asked for a place to stay. The willow tree also denied a place. Just then, he heard a spruce tree say, "Little bird, you can stay with me. My leaves are bushy and will keep you warm." And a pine tree said, "I can protect you from the cold North Wind." The juniper tree said that he could eat its berries all winter. That night, when the cold North Wind blew, all other trees lost their green leaves except the three kind trees. That is why spruce, pine, and juniper are evergreen trees even today.

14 Growing Good Corn

Farmer Peter won the gold medal for growing the best corn in the village. He became famous when the newspapers wrote about him. One day, a reporter was amazed to find Peter distributing his seeds to other farmers in the village. "If you distribute your seeds, how will you win the competition for growing the best corn next year?" the reporter asked.

"Sir," replied Peter, "the wind picks up pollen from crops and flowers and spreads it everywhere. So if my neighbours do not grow good crops, my field will suffer too. If I need to grow good corn, I must help my neighbours too." The reporter realised how wise the farmer was. To be happy one must make others happy too.

15 The Nutcracker Dwarf

Two boys were collecting hazelnuts in the woods. They wanted to eat the nuts but could not crack open the nuts with their teeth. Just then, a very tiny man came up to them and offered, "I can crack open the nuts for you. But will you give me some of your nuts in return?" The boys agreed.

They were amazed to see how he cracked the nuts. He placed the nuts in his jaws one at a time and simply crushed them! After cracking quite a number of nuts for the boys, the man asked for his share. Now, one boy was naughty and refused to give him the nuts. The dwarf got very angry and said, "If you do not keep your promise, I will break your teeth!" "Wait!" said the other boy, "Don't harm my friend. Here, you can have all my nuts." The naughty boy realised his friend's value and felt ashamed of his behaviour. He gave the dwarf some of his nuts and hugged his friend happily.

16 Ruff and Peter

Ruff was a cuddly German Shepherd and all the children loved him. However, there was one boy who disliked Ruff. It was Peter, an eight-year-old, who often hurled stones at the helpless animal. "What a mean boy he is!" thought Ruff while playing with the other children.

One day, there was a big storm. Peter had not returned from school. Soon, it became dark. His parents were very worried and his father went out to look for Peter.

"Why don't you take Ruff, I'm sure he can find your son!" suggested his neighbour. Ruff hated storms but he wanted to help Peter's father. After an hour, Ruff suddenly sniffed something. "Woof, Woof!" he barked and rushed to a huge pit. "Help! Help" they heard a faint voice. It was Peter, hanging on to a ledge precariously. Soon a crowd gathered and they all pulled him out.

Since then, Peter and Ruff are the best of friends.

17 Spotted

Alex and Anne were best friends. Alex had more toys than Anne and this annoyed Anne a lot. "Mummy, look, I have two rabbits but Alex has four. I have three pencils but Alex has five. He always has more," she complained. One evening, Alex and Anne went to pick berries. Anne picked ten but Alex still had more. He had picked twenty. Anne was really very upset. One day, Anne fell ill. She had spots all over her body. She felt itchy all the time. She couldn't go out and play with her friends. "Boo…hoo," she wailed in dismay. Just then Alex came to meet her. "Hey look," exclaimed Mummy, "Alex has no spots while you have so many." That made Anne very happy and brought a smile to her face.

165

18 The Stream

It was a hot summer day. Little Billy felt thirsty and worn out. He stopped for a while and saw a clear stream flowing. "The water is cold and my body is hot. Mamma said that it's not good to drink water when you are out in the sun," thought Billy. "What do I care," came the second thought. He drank the icy cold water. Suddenly, Billy felt weak and fainted the next moment. When his eyes opened, he found himself in bed with high fever. "The water of the stream was really bad," said Billy. "No, Billy, you are wrong. This happens when kids do not listen to their parents," replied his mother. Next time Billy saw the stream he remembered the fever and his mother's advice. "No I won't do it again," Billy said to himself.

19 Benny's Surprise

Benny's parents weren't there and his babysitter, Carol was taking care of him. Benny loved Carol very much. "I have a surprise for you, Benny!" said Carol. Benny couldn't believe his ears when Carol said, "We are going to the park today!" Together, the two of them went to the park and Benny sat on the red swing for a long time. Then, they fed the ducks in the pond. Benny loved watching the white ducks. When they finished feeding the ducks, Carol and Benny went for a quick brisk walk around the park. They stopped to watch the dogs playing with their owners. They talked to the other children. And finally, when Benny was tired, Carol took out a picnic basket and gave him sandwiches. "Wow, Carol! This is such a lovely surprise! I love you!" said Benny happily.

20 Terry's First Prize

Terry was a taxi driver. All day long he drove passengers in his yellow taxi, through the noisy city streets. "Oh, this noisy traffic gives me a headache!" lamented Terry. "Sometimes I wish I could live in a quiet place with no cars or trucks around," he said aloud.

One fine morning, a man knocked on Terry's door and said, "You've won the first prize in the lucky draw you had participated in last month!" "But where is the prize?" asked Terry curiously. "I'll give you a clue," said the man, "it has four wheels and is drawn by a horse!" Terry jumped up with joy. "It's a horse drawn carriage!" he said and rushed to see it.

Next day, Terry quit his job as a taxi driver and went back to his village where he plied passengers in his carriage on the quiet roads.

21 Boots and His Brothers

There was an oak tree beside the palace window that troubled the king. If you cut it, it grew more in size. "Whoever will cut the tree will get half my kingdom," declared the king.

People from far and wide came to try their luck. Boots and his brother also thought of trying their luck. One day, working in the forest, Boots heard a cutting sound, "Hey! What is that?" "You are silly, it's nothing," replied his brother. Boots went uphill and saw an axe that chopped by itself. "I was waiting for you to come. Take me to the hill and I will cut the oak tree," said the axe.

Boots took the axe to the king. He cut the oak tree in one stroke. Everyone cheered. In a moment, Boots became the hero.

22 Jeremy Fisher

Jeremy Fisher was a frog who loved to fish. One day, Jeremy wore his coat and took his fishing rod, some worms and set off fishing. "Today, I will invite Isaac Newton and Ptolemy Tortoise for a dinner of trout!" he thought and went to the stream. While he sat on his little green leaf boat and rowed with a thin reed, he saw shoals of fish scurrying about.

Jeremy Fisher was delighted. Suddenly, a huge trout passed by and rocked his tiny boat. Jeremy fell overboard and splashed into the water. The trout licked poor Jeremy and tried to gobble him. Somehow, he managed to escape from the huge fish and ran back home! Now Jeremy Fisher did not know what to give his guests for dinner. Isaac Newton got along with him some juicy salads and Ptolemy Tortoise ate weeds. And poor Jeremy Fisher had a butterfly sandwich.

23 Gwen's Lucky Day

Gwen hated going to school in the bus. She prayed to God for a bicycle. One fine morning, while going to school, Gwen saw a pink envelope at the door. She thought it would make a good bookmark and kept it in her bag.

In the evening when she returned home, Gwen saw that her parents searching for something. "I had left an important document on the table this morning. It was in a pink envelope. I can't find it anywhere now?" said her father. Gwen quickly took out the envelope and gave it to her father. "Thanks, Gwen. That was quite responsible of you. This paper is really very important," said her father waving the envelope in the air. Gwen's mother patted her and said, "As a reward, we'll get you a bicycle this weekend." It was indeed Gwen's lucky day.

24 Baxter Bear and Billy Bear

Cindy had two teddy bears, Baxter and Billy. While Baxter thought, "I am the best," Billy believed that nobody was better than him. Thus, the fight went on and the two hardly talked to each other. Cindy loved the two toys very much. "They are dear to me. Grandma gave them to me. I will keep them forever," she thought. Willy and Baxter had been good friends but they now started feeling jealous of each other. Each wanted to know whom Cindy loved the most. The argument went on endlessly. "You look horrible with those glasses! That's why Cindy loves me more," said Baxter. "And what about your straw hat. It makes you look like a silly cowboy. No wonder Cindy kisses me first when she comes back home," replied Billy. They spent the afternoon not talking to each other. At last, Cindy came from school. She ran to her room and picked up both the teddies. Billy and Baxter looked at each other. Cindy kissed and hugged both of them. "Perhaps she loves both of us equally," exclaimed the two.

25 Hilburt the Halibut

Hilburt the Halibut was a fish. He loved his home and surroundings, but had one big problem. While all the other fishes had lovely curves, Hilburt was flat. He felt he did not belong here. So he packed his bags and swam across the deep seas in search of someone like him. He searched everywhere but found none like him. There was the eight-legged octopus, the big bad shark and some crabs but they weren't any halibuts. One fine morning he bumped into Gertrude the grouper. "What are you doing here?" asked Gertrude. "I am searching for a friend," replied Hilburt. "I can be your friend!" said Gertrude excitedly. "But you're not a halibut!" said Hilburt. "But I am a fish and what difference does it make whether I am flat or round," explained Gertrude. So Hilburt was happy and they became good friends.

26 Melvin's Bad Temper

Melvin was a short-tempered boy. One day, his father decided to teach him a lesson. He brought a bag full of nails and said to him, "Melvin, whenever you lose your temper, hammer one nail into our fence." In the beginning, Melvin drove so many nails in the fence that he couldn't count them all! But as time passed, Melvin learnt to control his temper and didn't need to hammer any more nails. "Father, now I don't lose temper at all!" said Melvin one morning. "Good! Now you can pull out all the nails," said Father. When Melvin saw the holes the nails left, he understood what Father meant. "Words said in a bad temper can hurt people, even after saying sorry. Just like these holes which remain even after removing the nails," he realised. Melvin now tries not to lose his temper every now and then.

27 Looking for Mr. Bill

Timmy was staying at his grandma's house for the weekend. Grandma had many cats. Timmy loved her and all her little cats. "Where is Mr. Bill, Grandma?" asked Timmy while he searched for the furry white cat. Mr. Bill was his favourite cat.

"Meow!" Timmy suddenly saw Mr. Bill! Down the lane ran Mr. Bill and Timmy followed. He jumped fences, climbed trees, ran around homes and chased Mr. Bill all around. But the cat was too fast for him. Then Timmy realised that he was lost! He was scared and about to cry. Thankfully, there was a kind policeman watching Timmy and he took him back. And guess who was napping in Grandma's lawn? Mr. Bill!

28 Brave Little Bernie

Bernie was riding his bicycle when suddenly he bumped into a wall and landed in a heap. "Ouch, my leg hurts," wailed Bernie. Mummy took him to a doctor. The doctor put a big plaster on his leg. "No playing, walking or jumping around. You must rest." said the doctor. Bernie was quite upset. He had to stay at home while all his friends went out to play and have fun. "Mummy, please let me go out!" begged Bernie. Mummy thought for a while and had a great idea, "Let's call your friends home. They can all autograph your plaster." Every day his friends would come and write something on his plastered leg. Four weeks passed very quickly and soon, it was time to go to the doctor to have the plaster removed. Bernie was very proud of his plaster so it hangs on the wall of his room, even today.

29 Weepy Wilma

Little Wilma was four years old. It was her first day at school. In the morning, Mummy and Daddy drove Wilma to school. A man who looked like a policeman was standing at the gate. He was not letting the parents enter the school. "Only children allowed!" he chuckled. Soon a plump lady took Wilma's hand and smiled at her. Wilma was terrified! Why had Mummy left her alone with this lady? Wilma began to weep. She wept through study time, naptime and playtime. She wept the next day too, and the day after that! But on the fourth day, Wilma played on the swings during playtime and the other children said, "Look how high Wilma can swing!" She was happy and made many friends. Wilma never wept in school again.

30 Puffer Bunny

There was a bunny named Puffer, who lived with his siblings in a big white house. All day, he would play with them in their front yard. One day, while playing, Puffer Bunny hopped a little too far and he was long gone before the children could find him. He saw a tiny burrow and peered into it. He was surprised to see another bunny inside. "My name is Penny," she said, "come and see my family." Puffer hopped inside and saw three tiny bunnies in the pit. They were napping. "Just like my family!" said Puffer smilingly. He had a great time playing in the grassy meadows with Penny. His siblings back home were very worried. They thought a fox must have gobbled him. They were delighted when Puffer returned the next day!

Contents

The Story of the Month: The Run-around Clock

The Story of the Month

The Run-around Clock

01 The Run-around Clock

The alarm clock stood by the bed everyday and ticked every minute. The poor clock was feeling sad, "No one hears me tick all day and night! They only hear me when my alarm goes off at eight in the morning!" "That is what you are supposed to do!" said Chester, the China dog. "I am bored and tired of just ticking away!" sighed the alarm clock.

The alarm clock looked outside and saw that it was just dawn. It was only five in the morning and there were three more hours before his alarm would ring. "I will go out for a small run," thought the clock. He hopped off the shelf and went to the lawn. No sooner had he walked a little, he came face to face with a huge brown dog. The animal growled and barked at him and chased the clock down the road. Just then, a newspaper delivery boy almost ran over the clock. The alarm clock had a narrow escape. "Oh! It is just an hour since I left home and I am already wishing that I was home!" sighed the clock.

Just when he crossed the road to go back home, he found a huge machine with a large brush charging towards him. It was the road-cleaning machine. The alarm clock was drenched in icy cold water and scrubbed clean by the brush. "I want to go home!" cried the clock. But there was more to come his way. A man was clearing the garbage cans in the neighbourhood. He saw the alarm clock lying on the floor, picked it up and threw it into a trashcan. He thought that the clock was just a piece of junk.

The poor alarm clock managed to get out of the trashcan and hopped onto the road. Thankfully, he saw that he was just two houses away from his own home. The alarm clock took a look at his hands and almost panicked. "It is ten minutes to eight! I need to rush back home to ring my alarm on time!" he cried and got up to run into his house. Just then, a little kitten saw the clock. She licked the clock's face and purred. Then, the kitten dragged the clock in its house. "Why! It's Mitty, the Kitty! I am back home!" said the alarm clock happily. "You indeed are!" replied Chester the China dog.

At precisely eight, the alarm clock gave out his loudest ring, 'Trrrrrrrrrriinnnnnnnnnng!" The children and their parents woke up with big bright smiles on their faces. "There goes our alarm clock! On time, as always!" said Mother. The alarm clock was so happy to be back home! From that day onwards, the alarm clock never complained about ticking away time.

02 The Missing Pig

Arnold and Peter often took their pig, Ham, with them whenever they went out to play. One day, while Sam and Joe were playing, Ham was standing under a tree. Suddenly, Peter noticed that Ham was missing. "Where's Ham?" asked Peter. The two of them started searching for him. "Ham! Ham! Where are you?" shouted Arnold. They looked all around the field but could see no sign of Ham. "Let's go and see if he's gone towards the windmill. He often goes to play with the pigs in Farmer Grey's farm behind the windmill," suggested Peter. So the two boys walked towards the windmill. Suddenly, Arnold's eyes fell on a fox in the hedges near the windmill. "Oh! I hope Ham is safe," Arnold said a silent prayer. "Oink! Oink!" the boys heard a familiar grunt. They looked back and saw Ham standing near the fence of the windmill and ran to him. Ham was staring at the hedges. "Don't be scared. Let's go home," said Peter. The boys caressed Ham and smiled.

03 Adventurous Alex

Alex did not like the river like the other fish did. He longed to get away to a new place in search of more adventure. One day, an old and wise fish told everyone about the oceans, the whales and the dolphins. Alex was very curious and decided to follow the old fish to bigger waters in search of more excitement.

Alex was very excited by the new sights in the deep blue ocean. At first, he was scared of the big fishes and tried to hide. Soon, he found a cave and rested there for the night. He also found plenty of food nearby. The next morning, the big fish went her own way, but Alex decided to stay behind. He was happy at last to find a home he liked.

04 The Story of Creation

Long, long ago there lived a very big giant named Melu. He lived high above the clouds. He kept himself very clean by continually rubbing himself with his hands. The dead skin that fell off his body was kept in a pile that grew bigger every day. Melu decided to make the earth with the dead skin that he had collected. After the earth was made, Melu created two human beings much smaller than himself, with the remaining dead skin. Melu's brother Tau Tana appeared and wished to assist his brother. He made the noses but placed them upside down. One day, it rained and rained on earth until the people started drowning because the water could enter their noses. Melu saw their despair and turned their noses the other way. The noses now faced downwards. The people were very grateful to Melu.

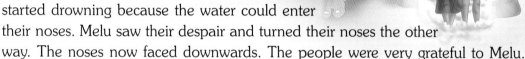

05 Lenny the Flying Inventor

Lenny loved to invent new things. One day he decided he wanted to fly. He began working in his workshop and after two weeks he had created wings out of wax and balsa wood. Mac, Lenny's friend helped him to strap on the wings. "Here we go," said Lenny. He ran towards the crest of the hill and was soon lifted high and then higher and higher. He soared high above, but soon the wax on the wings began to melt due to the sun's heat. Lenny began to worry because he did not know how to land on the ground and he was afraid that the wax might all melt before he reached earth. Just then, a little angel appeared and helped Lenny reach the ground safely. Lenny thanked the angel and asked, "Who are you? How did you know I needed help?" The angel smiled and said, "All good little boys have an angel who takes care of them. For every good deed that they do, their angel helps them when they are in trouble. I am your angel."

06 Long Bony Fingers

One day Sammy went to Bobby's house to read some new scary stories. Before he left, his father said, "Sammy, you must return before dark." But, Sammy sat reading all evening. Finally, he had to walk back in the dark. Sammy was scared. Suddenly, he heard someone right behind him saying, "Guess what I can do with my long bony fingers?" Sammy was frightened and raced home. While crossing the lane, he heard the voice again, "Guess what I can do with my long bony fingers?" Sammy ran into his room and hid under his bed, and he once again heard, "Guess what I can do with my long bony finger?" Sammy somehow gathered courage and looked at the 'voice'. Imagine his relief and surprise when he realised that it was his father in a monster costume! Sammy never disobeyed his father again.

07 The Rocky Mountain Train

The Red train carried many people across the mountains. The number of people who travelled by the Red train grew day by day. "At this rate, the Red train will break down one day," said the engine driver. But the driver liked to listen to the song that the passengers sang as the train chugged along the mountainside. One day, the packed train was unable to go up the mountain.

"How will we reach home?" said the worried passengers. All of a sudden a little boy jumped out of the train. "There's a tunnel nearby. Let's look for it. That will save us from going up the mountains." The passengers started looking for the tunnel and went in different directions. At last they found the old tunnel and cleared the tracks and the undergrowth. Soon the Red Train was running through the tunnel and once again, the train was filled with the joyful song of the passengers.

08 The Flowers

"Rose is the most beautiful flower," said little Louisa. "But I think lilies are prettier than roses," replied her sister Caroline. "I simply love its colour." Mary was listening to her younger sisters talking about flowers. She said, "When you are talking of the flowers, how can you forget the violet? I think violets are the best."

Their mother heard them talking and said, "My dear, each flower teaches us something. While violet stands for modesty, lily teaches innocence and rose shows love for God and all its creatures." Now Louisa, Caroline and Mary found all the flowers equally beautiful!

09 The Three Butterflies

Red, Blue and Yellow were three beautiful butterflies. When they were young, their mother had told them to be loyal to each other. The thick black cloud wanted to put the solidarity of the sisters to test. One day, when they were visiting a garden, he splashed down heavily on their fragile wings.

"Let's run to the Gulmohar tree!" said Red.

"I will only allow Red to take shelter on my red flowers!" said the Gulmohar tree.

"If you do not allow my sisters, I will not stay here," replied Red.

Then Yellow suggested that they should rest on the beautiful Amaltas tree.

"Only Yellow is allowed here," said the Amaltas.

"My sisters are more precious to me," said Yellow angrily.

Finally, when the blue Morning Glory also refused, the three butterflies flew away hand in hand. The cloud was happy and cleared the path for the sun to shine.

10 Audun and the Bear

Long, long ago there lived a young man called Audun in Iceland. One spring, he decided to sail to Norway.

Audun reached Greenland with the captain of the ship. He was overwhelmed by the beauty of the majestic polar bear. He gave all his savings to buy a bear. "I will gift this treasure to the king of Denmark," he thought.

The king was delighted to receive the gift and in return offered Audun a stay at his palace for as long as he wished. Three years passed by and Audun began to miss his mother. "I must get back to my mother now." He thanked the king for his hospitality and as a token from the king, took along with him a large purse bearing the royal crest and full of gold coins. Audun reached home, a rich and prosperous man.

11 Abiyoyo the Giant

A magician was in trouble because he was always playing tricks on people. He had a magic wand that made things disappear— Zoop! Zoop! One day, the people of the town went to him and said, "You better leave the town and take your magic wand with you." The magician left the town and went away. Now the people believed that a terrible giant called Abiyoyo lived somehere on the outskirts of their town and would come and attack them someday. One morning, they felt that the earth was shaking and a thundering sound was coming from a distance. "Run! Abiyoyo is here! Run!" screamed the people and ran to save their lives. Abiyoyo was really very huge. Just then, the magician appeared and lifted his magic wand in the air and—Zoop! The giant disappeared. The people thanked the magician for saving their lives and asked him to come back and live with them.

12 Mrs. Bruno's Pies

Mrs. Bruno baked delicious hot apple pies. Everyone eagerly waited for her apple pies and before anyone could realise, they were over! Mrs. Bruno soon became famous.

But Mrs. Bruno was worried. "What should I do? I love baking apple pies but when I go to answer the door or pick up the phone, the pies in the oven get burnt. My shop is so far that by the time I walk the distance, the pies become cold," she lamented.

She thought over her problem, "I think I'll have to stop baking pies," she decided

The customers were very disappointed to hear that there would be no more pies. When they came to know why, they came up with a bright idea. They would come to Mrs. Bruno's house to collect the hot delicious pies! Mrs. Bruno was very happy.

13 The Obstacle in Our Path

Once upon a time there lived a just king. One day, the king placed a huge boulder in the middle of the road to judge his people. Many of the king's courtiers and ministers passed by the road complaining how little the king did for his people. Even though the boulder was blocking the road, no one tried to move it away. Finally, a poor peasant came by. He was carrying a heavy sack full of vegetables and fruits, but still he tried to move the boulder. After a lot of hard work, the peasant succeeded in moving the boulder. As soon as the boulder moved, the peasant found a bagful of gold coins and a note from the king that said, "Keep the gold coins as a reward, you are a responsible citizen!"

That is why we say that every obstacle in our path is a chance to improve our lives.

14 The Greedy Toy Clown

Ann had lots of toys. There were fluffy teddy bears, pretty Russian dolls, a beautiful Barbie, and one wooden toy clown in her cupboard. Nobody liked the toy clown because he was very greedy. At night he would tiptoe into the kitchen and eat all the food. One day, Ann received a wonderful present—a tiny stove, with little saucepans, and a kettle. So, Ann made some cookies and delicious muffins for her toys. As soon as Ann was gone, the greedy clown crept into the kitchen. There were enough muffins and also a glass of milk to fill his hungry tummy! He was so excited that he started dancing. Just then, his sleeve caught the handle of the saucepan and he toppled and fell to the ground. "Serves you right," said Ann when she came and saw him. He promised not be greedy again and Ann bandaged his arm and kissed him.

15 Mountain Adventure

Jamie and Jasmine were in Switzerland with their parents. They were very excited, as they would be learning how to ski. There was a big, brown dog called Bruno in their hotel and they made friends with him. The next day, Jamie and Jasmine put on their special skiing jackets, trousers and boots. In the beginning, they fell down a few times. However, after some practice they learnt skiing. One morning, when they arrived early to ski, there was no one around. Jamie and Jasmine went skiing down the steep mountain. A little later, Jasmine heard a low, rumbling noise from the other side of the mountain. Suddenly, she saw a huge mass of ice moving towards them. "It's an avalanche," shouted Jasmine. The rumbling noise grew louder and suddenly everything was dark. Jamie and Jasmine's were stuck behind a big boulder of ice. The rescue helicopter went in search of the children along with Bruno. Suddenly, Bruno started barking. He had found the two children. The police arrived with their parents and picked up the little children and took them home. Bruno, Jamie and Jasmine became the best of friends.

16 The Mushrooms

One day, Catherine's mother sent her to the backyard of their house to look for mushrooms as Catherine's father loved mushrooms. After some time Catherine returned with a bag of fresh mushrooms. "Look at the bright red and purple mushrooms I have got Mama!" She said excitedly. "But these are poisonous mushrooms!' replied her mother anxiously. "Didn't you find any which were brown or white in colour?" she asked. "I did, but they were so ugly, that I left them there!" replied Catherine.

"My dear, those plain and ugly ones are actually edible and the best ones too," she explained, "You should not judge everything by its appearance alone." Catherine thought for a while and nodded her head. She had learnt an important lesson in life.

17 Aniz the Shepherd Boy

Once upon a time there was a small shepherd boy called Aniz. He had a very cruel master. Aniz was very fond of playing the flute. When he played, all the animals circled around him in adoration. Aniz loved the animals and they loved him. "I have kept you for work, not for playing the flute," said the master and often beat Aniz. One day the landlord saw a beautiful rabbit in his dream. "I want the rabbit at any cost," said the landlord. He ordered his sons, "Go and find the rabbit else I will not give you my property."

All the animals knew where the rabbit was. But none of them told the landlord's sons where they could find him. When the animals heard Aniz playing the flute, they rushed out to meet him and the rabbit also came out of his burrow. Aniz's master realised that love can do what you can never do by force.

18 The Fishes and the Swan

Some fishes lived in a lovely garden pond surrounded by beautiful tulips. One day, Father Fish popped out of the water to have a look and was frightened by what he saw and dived down to tell the other fishes that he had seen a big animal. Mother Fish said, "I think, it's a cat we must be careful because cats eat fishes." Baby Fish was annoyed on hearing this and decided to frighten the 'cat.' He quietly swam up and moved straight to the animal's back. But instead of feeling soft skin, he felt cold metal. He was surprised to see a metal swan. He told the other fishes, "That is not a cat. It's a lovely metal swan. Come and see." Soon, the other fishes were also leaping and jumping on the metal swan. What a lovely time they had!

19 The Animal Train

Everyday the goods train would pass through the jungle and the animals would look at it with curiosity. "I wish even we could get inside the train and travel," said the deer one day. The giraffe and the cheetah nodded wistfully. One day, the animals went to the elephant for some advice. The fox said, "Brother, you have worked with humans. Can you request the train driver to let us travel to the next jungle? I can meet my relatives there." The elephant agreed to try. Next day, the animals accompanied the elephant towards the tracks. When the train stopped at a red signal, the elephant walked towards the engine driver and lifted his trunk first towards the train and then towards the animals. The driver understood the elephant's request and asked for the guard's permission. Both the driver and the guard loved animals so they allowed the animals to come in. All the animals cheered for the elephant and hopped onto the train. What a lovely sight it was!

20 Mama Moo on the Swing

Mama Moo, the cow, disliked her daily routine of chewing cud and staring blankly at the world. She wanted some fun. So every afternoon, she sneaked out of farmer Gary's farm and came to the park to sit on the swing. Now Mama Moo was really fat and couldn't move the swing herself. She sat on it, stretched one leg to the ground to take grip and pushed hard. But alas! The swing never moved. So a kind pig agreed to help her. Everyday, the pig pushed from behind while Mama Moo enjoyed. One day, the other cows followed her to the park and saw her sitting on the swing. "While every afternoon we chew cud, Mama Moo comes here to have fun!" complained one of them. "Let's teach her a lesson," said another. That night the cows came to the swing and loosened its screws. Next afternoon, when Mama Moo sneaked out of the farm, they followed her and hid behind the bushes. Like always the pig stood behind and Mama Moo sat on the swing proudly. But lo! The swing creaked, the iron chain snapped and Mama Moo fell down with a thud. "Enjoy yourself!" shouted the other cows and ran away.

21 From the Elephant Pit

Once upon a time, a hunter had dug a pit to trap a wild elephant. But instead of an elephant, a lion that was chasing a deer fell into the pit. When the hunter came, the lion pleaded, "Please save me, I shall always be grateful to you."

The kind hunter trusted the lion and pulled him out of the pit. The lion thanked the hunter and went his way. A few months passed by. The hunter fell very ill and had nothing to eat, as he could no longer hunt. When the lion came to know about the hunter's condition, he brought fresh meat and vegetables for him. The hunter was very touched and thanked the lion for saving his life.

22 The Ten Fairies

Minnie was very pampered. Her parents really pampered her and spoilt her. But, when Minnie grew up, she had a tough time. There were many things to do in the house and at school. Minnie's mother would often scold her. "Why are you so disorganised? What do you do the whole day?" she would say. Minnie was very upset. One day, she cried bitterly. "I wish I had some fairies to help me in my work. Dear God! Hear my prayer," she said longingly.

No sooner did she say this, than ten tiny fairies appeared before her and said, "We are here to help you and will remain hidden in your fingers. Just clap your hands." So, the fairies helped Minnie clean her cupboard and organise her room. Minnie's mother was surprised to see this sudden change in her and praised her. But, Minnie never gave away her secret!

23 The Packet of Chocolates

Once there was a girl called Jennifer whose parents were very rich. But Jennifer was a very untidy and careless girl. One summer day, her father, who had just returned from Singapore after a business trip, gifted a packet of chocolates to her. Jennifer kept the chocolates on the chair carelessly instead of keeping them in the refrigerator and went out to play with her friends. In the evening, when she returned home, she sat down on that chair. Suddenly, she got up and wailed loudly. She realised that she had sat on the chocolates that had melted in the heat. Her mother came running to her room. To her dismay, they saw that all the chocolates were crushed and had stained Jennifer's new dress. From that day, Jennifer learned to keep her things in order.

24 The Cross Little Girl

Belinda had a terrible temper. She threw her toys around if she didn't get things her way. The toys were very unhappy. One day, Belinda couldn't find the tin soldier and she threw a big tantrum. All her toys were upset. So, when she squeezed into her cupboard shelf to pretend that it was her house, all the toys locked her up inside! "Let me out!" she begged. But the toys would not hear her pleas. "You are always hurting us! We don't want to play with you!" yelped the China Dog. "I promise I will be good tempered from now on!" said Belinda. They let her out and ever since then nobody had come across a girl as sweet as Belinda!

25 Hamilton the Hamster

Hamilton the hamster lived with a butcher. Hamilton was lonely and bored and would try to catch the attention of the customers. "I wish someone would take me home with them," he often thought.

One day, a kind looking man came by and saw Hamilton trying to catch his attention. The man came everyday for a few days and started liking Hamilton but he knew that the butcher wouldn't give him away. So he did not say anything to the butcher. Hamilton too started loving this new visitor. So he took a piece of paper and wrote, "Will you please take me home?" and held it up for the man to see. The man was surprised to see a hamster that could write!

Hamilton was soon packed off with the kind man to his new home!

26 Three Pumpkin Pirates

A big pirate ship dropped anchor on a remote island on the Halloween night. There were three pirates in the ship and all three had big pumpkin heads! They were searching for a treasure. "Dig here for the treasure, men!" commanded Captain Pumpkin. The other two pirates dug for hours. But alas! They found nothing! Just when they were about to give up and return to the ship, they heard some children laughing. The Captain's eyes gleamed in excitement. "It seems like a village there. Come follow me, we will surely find treasures in the village homes!"

The pumpkin pirates saw children, dressed as witches and ghosts, distributing candies. "Trick or treat!" cried the children and gave the pirates a handful of candies. While coming out they heard the sound of drums from another house and went to see what it was. Here the family members were dressed in military uniform and playing drums. "My! My! What wonderful costumes you have! Happy Halloween!" said one of the pirates. "Trick or Treat!" the man of the house said and gave them a very heavy bag. The pirates went off to their ship happily and rummaged the bags for gifts. But lo! It had only sand. "And these are not candies either, but pebbles!" cried another pirate. "How dare they cheat us? Let's go get them!" said Captain Pumpkin angrily.

When they reached the spot they found that the children had left, the sound of drums had ceased and surprisingly there were no houses there either. "Where's everybody?" asked Captain Pumpkin. "I think those were ghosts!" said one pirate. "After all it's Halloween!" explained another. "Hurry, let's run to the ship," commanded Captain Pumpkin and the three pumpkin pirates sailed away on their ship.

27 Chicky Chick

One day Chicky, a little chick was walking along the country path when an apple bumped on his little head. "Oh dear!" jumped the little chick in alarm. "What could that be!" he wondered. Frightened and confused, he overlooked the apple lying on the ground. "I think a cloud has hit my head. I am sure the sky is falling down," he thought aloud, "It will kill all of us in no time. I must inform our king immediately." Thinking this, the little chick started running to the king. On his way, he met Henny the hen. Henny called out, "Hey Chicky, where are you going. Can I go along with you?" "Hello Henny! The sky is falling. I must inform the king immediately," he said anxiously. So Henny the hen joined him and together they started running to the king. This way everyone from Dapple Duck, Weepy Sheepy and Larky Turkey all joined the little chick. Soon they met Mr. Fox on their way and asked him where the king was. "Come with me. I'll show you the way," said Mr Fox and led them to his den. But clever Chicky understood his intention in time and all of them ran away to save their life.

28 The Truthful Dove

Once, on a stormy night, a dove and a bat asked an owl for shelter. The owl lived in a hollow tree and unwillingly let the two animals enter his house. He was quite selfish and vain and did not like to share his food with anyone either. The bat was very sly. He knew that if he praised the owl's wisdom, courage and generosity, the owl would be happy and he would get a good share of the food in return. So the bat flattered the owl and the owl was very pleased. He said "Here my dear friend, help yourself to more food." But the dove did not like to flatter others and remained silent. The owl loved flattery and was angry at the dove for keeping quiet. He threw the dove out of the house. By now, the storm was almost over and the dove flew away to meet her family.

29 Miri and the Gardener

Miri was a very pretty fairy who lived on a giant oak tree in a forest. But she was suffering from a strange illness that no one had been able to cure.

One day a gardener was walking through the forest. He was carrying a very beautiful butterfly in a little piece of net. This butterfly had magical powers. If it rested on anyone's eyes, that person would be cured of every illness.

While the gardener was resting under the shade of the giant oak tree, he heard someone sobbing. The gardener climbed up the tree and saw Miri crying. Suddenly, a pigeon flew up to him and said, "Do you have any cure for our fairy? She's very ill." The gardener was very kind. He took out the butterfly from the net and placed it on the fairy's eyes. And Lo! Miri was hale and hearty again.

30 The Singing Birds

The field was full of green grass and lovely flowers. Two birds had built a nest in a tall tree in one corner of the field. Soon, the female bird laid five tiny eggs. "They are so wonderful," she said. And both the birds burst into a joyous song.

After two weeks, all the eggs hatched and out popped five tiny yellow birds. When the little birds grew up, they flew away and made their own nests and sang their own songs.

One day, Father Bird was very quiet. "Why don't you sing?" asked Mother Bird.

"Look how everything changes. Soon we will also have to leave this tree. All the leaves have fallen as winter is round the corner," he said. So the next day, the birds flew in search of a warm place where flowers always bloomed and birds always sang.

31 A Howling Halloween

Paul and Andy were walking home on a dark, rainy night on thirty-first of October. It was Halloween, the festival of witches and ghosts. Suddenly, a black cat appeared before them. "Meow!" it cried and disappeared in the bushes. Everything around was silent except for the crisp sound of the pouring rain.

After sometime it stopped raining. "Andy, let's hurry up before it starts pouring again!" cried Paul. After a while, Andy and Paul passed by an old, dark house when they heard a low, howling sound. "Whooooooo-Whooooooo!" "I think it's a dog," said Andy, trying not to be scared. Again they heard the strange sound and this time they decided to enter the house. "Maybe there's someone inside that house!" thought Andy. They passed through the old rusty gates and then pushed open the main door. A spider's web greeted Andy and Paul as they entered the dark and dusty room. They walked further ahead into a large room.

When they entered the room, they saw a dull fire in the fireplace. Above that hung a mirror in which they saw colourful lights reflect. , a big hand with long nails emerged from the mirror and caught hold of Paul's neck with one hand and Andy's neck with the other and dragged them to another dark room.

Paul and Andy couldn't believe their eyes. There in the room they saw so many witches and monsters and ghosts. The witches were dancing and the wizards and monsters were drinking a special brew. The two boys forgot their fear and joined the party and danced until dawn. Everyone agreed that it was the best Halloween party ever.

"See you next year," said the witches to the boys, when they left next morning.

Contents

The Story of the Month: The Singing Shell

The Story of the Month

The Singing Shell

01 The Singing Shell

Once upon a time there was a young boy. His name was Brown and he lived in the mountains. Brown had no friends and he was sad and lonely. One day a kind shepherd saw him sitting there. "Who are you, my boy? Why are you sitting alone?" asked the shepherd. "I don't have a family. I don't even have friends, what do I do?" "Why, you can go down and make friends there," advised the shepherd. So, Brown decided to go down on a vacation.

Brown walked and walked downhill till he saw trees and green grasses around him. "On the mountain it was just white snow spread all over. Its different here," thought Brown. He further went on and suddenly saw something shining in the distance.

Brown wondered, "Hey! What is it? It looks so dazzling and sparkling." He saw an old man passing by and stopped him and asked, "Could you please tell me what is that?" "Dear child, that is a sea and it has lots and lots of creatures inside. Go and see them, then you will understand better."

Brown got excited when he heard about the mermaids and mermen. "I will surely go and see. They seem to be strange, beautiful creatures." He saw children playing at the beach. Brown too started playing with them and had lots of fun. But, he really wanted to know about the marine life. He did not know how to swim and sighed, "Only if I could swim."

There was a mermaid, Maria sitting a few yards away from Brown. He hardly saw her but she heard him. Brown was lost in his thoughts when she suddenly came up to him. "Hello, I am Maria. Would you be my friend?" Brown rose to his feet, hardly able to speak. He had never seen a mermaid earlier and wondered, "Wow! What a beautiful creature." He felt as if he was dreaming. Brown sat on Maria's back and she showed him the beautiful sea world. "What a wonderful life, but alas! I have to go back to the mountain, again," groaned Brown. "Don't worry I will take you to the sea whenever you wish," replied Maria. She took a shell and let a small wave break into it. Emptying the shell she gave it to Brown. "Whenever you miss the sea just put this shell close to your ear and you will hear the waves coming and going." Brown felt delighted, "I don't mind going back to the mountain. Now, I can enjoy both the sea and the mountain. That's fantastic." Thus, whenever he felt lonely and sad, Brown put the shell close to his ear and heard the gush of water coming and going. Brown was never sad again.

02 The Lonely Deer

Once on a tiny desert island near the sea, there lived a young deer, all by himself. He was very lonely as there was no one to play with him. He did not even know how to get out of the island.

One day a fish took pity on the lonely deer and told him to follow him to the big forest where there were many deer. The deer tried hard to swim but could not. Next day, a swan tried to teach the deer how to fly but that the deer gave up.

Six months later, an elephant passed by the island. "Come onto my back, little deer. I'll take you to the big forest," said the elephant loudly. He bent down and the deer hopped onto his back. "Wow! I'll never be lonely again," cried the deer in joy. Soon, the elephant and the deer became very good friends.

03 Jeffrey the Goose

One day Jeffrey the goose and his friends sneaked out of their pen and went to the riverbank. Suddenly, two huge dogs saw the geese and charged at them. Alas! They slipped on the dew-covered grass and fell into the river. The geese fled to their pens. The farmer heard the noise and came to see what had happened. He was very cross when he came to know that the geese had left their pens. "You must never leave this pen. You are safe here. If you go out, someone may attack you," he scolded them. Jeffrey decided to sneak out once more, but the others refused to join him. "It was so much fun by the riverbank," Jeffrey chuckled and told the other geese after coming back. One day, Jeffrey did not come back. When the farmer went to look for him, he found Jeffrey lying in a pit, hurt and wounded. "A car ran over me," he wailed. The farmer brought Jeffrey home and bandaged him. Jeffrey had learnt his lesson. He never disobeyed the farmer ever again.

04 Audrey's Adventure

One day, Audrey decided to go and visit her aunt. She had a lot of fun and ate a little cake and drank some lemonade at her aunt's place. "I must go home now. It's getting dark." She put on her coat and wore her fluffy mittens and said goodbye to her aunt. Audrey's house was just a ten minute walk from her aunt's. As she walked, Audrey started humming. She even did a little jiggle. There were five days left for her birthday. She was busy thinking about what she would do when suddenly, she bumped into a tree. It was quite dark. She looked around and didn't know where she was. She had lost her way. "Oh" she wailed, "I don't know where I am." She sat under the tree and started sobbing. Suddenly, she felt a dog licking her face. "Oh Buddy," I am glad you found me. Just then, her father appeared with a torch and picked her up in his arms. "Audrey, you must come home before it's dark. We were so worried." Audrey wiped her tears and gave her dad a big hug.

05 The Elephant That Skied

Elsa was not at all like the other Elephants. All day, her family would wallow in the muddy pool but she would stand in the rain and enjoy the water trickling down her skin. "Come, Elsa. This mud is warm like chocolate," her brother would call. But Elsa did not go. Her favourite pastime was trying to float on the big lotus leaves in the pond but alas! She would always sink down like a stone. But Elsa never gave up trying.

In the pond lived her friends, the two frogs. They helped her and after lots of hard practice, Elsa finally learnt to float. "Hey look! I am floating!" she shouted one day. A photographer saw her. He said, "Why don't you come to my country? There are snow-covered mountains, you would love it." Elsa flew with him in an aeroplane. The people loved Elsa and came to watch her skiing. They even awarded her a gold medal. When Elsa returned to her pond she showed her gold medal to her frog friends. "Elsa is a famous Elephant!" said everyone.

06 Bitsy's Promise

The smell of freshly baked cookies woke up Bitsy Bunny. "These cookies are for your grandmother," said Mother Rabbit to Bitsy. "Shall I take them to her?" asked Bitsy. "Well…you must promise that you will not talk to strangers or peep into the river or stop to see the wild flowers on your way," said Mother Rabbit. "It's a promise!" said Bitsy and hopped away. On the way, some beautiful wild flowers caught Bitsy's attention and he was about to touch them when he remembered his mother's warning. Bitsy immediately withdrew her hand and started walking ahead. Bitsy yearned to see the frisky fishes in the river flowing alongside. But he remembered his mother's words of caution, "The river has crocodiles too!" Bitsy was scared and hurried along. After a while, he saw a pile of hay before him. "Do you want some?" asked a man who was walking towards him. He was about to reply but remembered that he had promised not to talk to strangers. Bitsy ran as fast as he could and reached grandma's house. As soon as he entered, the telephone rang. It was Mother Rabbit, "You've been a good bunny and kept your promise. Now you can also have the cookies!" "Yippee!" shouted Bitsy and relished the tasty cookies.

07 The Camel's Hump

Long ago there lived a very lazy camel in the desert. If ever someone asked him to work, he would snort angrily and say, "Hump!" The other animals would get very annoyed at this. One day they went to a wizard for help. "Why don't you work?" asked the wizard. "Hump!" grunted the camel. Alas! To his utter amazement, he saw his back puffing up like a mountain. "Here's your hump!" said the wizard. "From now on, you shall work in the desert without food and survive on your hump, because it's full of fat which you can use as food!" said the wizard. Ever since then camels have a hump on their back.

08 Hoo-Hoo's Party

Hoo- Hoo, the greedy owl, hadn't eaten for days. He wondered what to do. Suddenly a wonderful idea came to his mind, "I will throw a party at midnight and invite, Taylor the mouse, Soft-Ears the rabbit, Singer the nightingale and Frisky the squirrel. And that will be a delicious meal indeed!" he thought, chuckling to himself. "A grand party!" squeaked the mouse in delight. "And so much to eat!" said Singer when they heard about the party. "But why should the party begin at midnight?" thought Frisky after reading the invitation card carefully. So he told his friends, "Now, do as I say." At night, instead of going inside Hoo-Hoo's house, they all watched from a distance. Inside, a group of owls were talking very loudly. "Today is the grand feast!" they joked. But hours passed and none of the animals turned up. The other owls lost their patience and attacked Hoo-Hoo instead. Frisky and his friends jumped with joy and thanked him for saving their lives.

09 The Conceited Cow

There lived a very proud cow who always bragged about herself. One day, her little calf said to her, "Mother, I just saw an animal which was as big as a mountain!" "Oh! It's only the circus elephant. I can also make myself as big as him. Look!" So the cow began to blow herself out till she became broader and broader. Then she asked, "Was he this big?" "No Mother, he was even bigger," said the little calf. So the conceited cow continued to blow herself bigger and bigger. The little calf stood amazed at the sight. At last, the cow became so large that it couldn't breathe any more. Just then a fairy appeared and said, "Look, you are so proud of yourself but in your foolishness, you are now stuck in this position." When the cow begged for mercy and promised never to brag again, the fairy waved a wand and the cow returned to her usual size.

10 The Tinkle of the Goats' Bells

Joanna was sitting by the riverside while her goats grazed on the grass. Suddenly, she saw two men running towards the road with gunny bags. "Run faster, the police is around," she heard one of them say. One of the men slipped and fell down and his gunny bag opened. A glass-topped box came sliding out. Joanna was shocked to see that there were butterflies in the box. The man quickly picked up the box and rushed to a car standing nearby. His friend was waiting inside. "Oh! These must be Mr. Ray's butterflies. They were stolen yesterday," thought Joanna. She called all her goats and very soon, the road was filled with the herd of goats making it impossible for the car to move. Soon, the police arrived and arrested the thieves from the car. "The tinkle of your goats' bells signalled to us that something was wrong," said the police inspector to Joanna and thanked her.

11 Alan and the Aliens

Alan often wished he could meet an alien, who could tell him more about life on other planets. One night, Alan woke up from his sleep and heard strange noises. "Waa, Shaa, Goop, Cha." Alan sat up in bed and lo! Three strange figures stood before him. They looked like brinjals and had spots on them, and a metal antenna bulged out of their heads.

Alan was terrified. "Mum! Dad!" he shouted.

"We have come from Mars and want to be your friend" said one of them. "Oh, Aliens!" whispered Alan in wonder. "We know you like us. We have come all the way with a request because we know you can help us," said the second alien.

"We want you to tell the other humans that our planet is very beautiful. Tell them that they must keep their planet clean. They should not litter the surrounding and offend nature," said the third alien. The aliens disappeared all of a sudden. When Alan woke up in the morning, he couldn't find any evidence of the aliens' visit but he did remember what they had said.

12   Patrick Helps Mummy

One day little Patrick saw Mummy lying on the bed. "I am unwell dear," she said. Patrick felt very sad. He had never seen Mummy falling sick. Even Daddy was out of town. "I must help Mummy, afterall she needs rest." he thought. He ran to his room. It was so messy with clothes, books and toys scattered all around. Patrick started cleaning the room. He dusted the cabinets, picked up the books from the floor and arranged them properly. He tidied the room and kept everything in place. Then he went to the bathroom and bathed all by himself unlike other days when Mummy had a hard time making him take his bath. After that, he went to the kitchen and made a sandwich for Mummy. Imagine her surprise when she saw Patrick with a tray. "Thank you so much. That's so nice of you," she said. "I love you Mummy," said Patrick and gave her a big hug.

13   Where Did the Nuts Go?

A squirrel was hoarding nuts in the hole of a tree. A nuthatch discovered this hiding place and began stealing the nuts. The nuthatch didn't have teeth like the squirrel did so he took a nut in his beak and hammered it hard against the tree trunk. Crack! The nuts broke and the nuthatch happily ate them. One day, the squirrel was sleeping inside the hole when he heard the sound of nuts cracking and woke up. "Oh no!" he sighed when he saw the bird relishing his nuts. "How dare you eat my nuts?" he asked angrily. "These are mine," replied the nuthatch. Finally the nuthatch flew into the hole and dropped all the nuts to the ground. He did it day after day, only to annoy the squirrel more. Now at the bottom of the tree lived a mouse who was amazed to find nuts falling from the tree everyday. "God is so kind to me!" he thought. One day the squirrel scurried to the ground to search for the nuts. Alas! None of the nuts were there. "Where did the nuts go?" he thought. He was sure the nuthatch had eaten them and went to confront him. So, they fought forever while the mouse enjoyed the delicious nuts below!

14 Red Hat or Green Hat?

One day when Tim and Jim were playing in the field, a man walked between the two friends. He was wearing a cap, which was green on one side and red on the other. "Oh, What a lovely red cap!" complimented Tim, who could see only the red part of the cap. "No, the cap is green!" replied Jim. "How can it be green when I can clearly see that it's red," said Tim. "It's green and not red!" insisted Jim and a fierce argument followed between the two. The man heard them and stopped. He took off his cap and showed it to the two boys. "Ah! It's both green and red!" sighed Tim. "Yes!" said the man, "We often believe what we see and know and are not open to someone else's point of view." The two boys nodded and looked at each other. They had learnt an important lesson today.

15 Pinky the Buffalo

Pinky the buffalo was only two inches tall. None of the animals of the jungle liked Pinky. But nobody knew how courageous Pinky really was. One day, a group of woodcutters came to the jungle. Pinky saw them and said, "I must warn everybody against these woodcutters." She rushed to climb up a tree. "How dare you climb up my tree?" roared Hootie the owl.

"Please, let me climb up. I need to warn everybody!" pleaded Pinky. But the owl refused to listen. Pinky ran to the next tree but a monkey sitting atop the tree didn't allow Pinky to do so either. Pinky quickly hid behind a shrub and grunted so loudly that the woodcutters were terrified and ran away. All the animals thanked Pinky for saving their lives and she soon became one of the most-loved buffaloes.

16   The Honest Farmer

One day, a poor farmer was ploughing the fields when he found an earthen jar on the ground. He lifted the lid and found gold coins inside. He ran home to tell his wife about his find. "God is great," said his wife, "He has sent a treasure for us." "Don't even think about it," said the farmer angrily, "How can I take the coins when the field belongs to my master?" However, their neighbour heard the farmer and his wife talking. At night, the neighbour went to the fields to find the earthen jar. But when he lifted the lid, he found mud instead! Meanwhile as the farmer and his wife slept, gold coins showered on his hearth. Next morning, when they got up, the farmer exclaimed in delight, "Now, I can accept these riches since God has sent them for me." The farmer and his wife became rich and bought their own fields.

17   Helena's New Pet

One day, while playing in the garden, Helena found a Myna lying on the ground. One of its wings was broken and the little bird was squeaking in pain. Helena carefully picked up the bird. "Mom, see what I've found," she shouted. Her mother came out to see what the matter was. "Mom, can we take this bird to the hospital? Look, it needs attention." Mom drove Helena and the bird to the animal hospital. The doctor there bandaged the bird's broken wing and said it would take a week to heal.

Every afternoon after returning from school, Helena would run to look at the Myna. Over the days, Helena grew very fond of the little bird. One day, Helena asked her mother, "Mom, can we keep it? I've even thought of a name…Teeny." Helena's mother nodded her head and smiled.

November

18 Norah and the Tree Elf

Norah has been sick for a long time. Everyday the doctor came in the morning and examined Norah. "You'll soon be fine, dear," he assured her. But Norah showed no sign of recovery. From her bed, Norah watched the old Margo tree that her grandfather had planted years back. One evening, Norah looked at the tree and remembered her grandpa sitting under the tree in his armchair. "I wish he was here. He could have asked the Tree Elf to cure me of my sickness," she sighed. Suddenly there was a cracking sound and out came a tiny man from the tree. He hopped in through the window and sat near Norah. "Who are you?" asked a frightened Norah. "Don't panic. I'm the Tree Elf and mean no harm," said the dwarf. Norah felt a chill running through her as the dwarf rubbed some herbs all over her body. She dozed off to sleep. Next morning Norah woke up and felt refreshed. Her body was not in pain anymore. Quite thrilled, Norah ran down to tell her parents!

19 The Lonely Old Man

An old man lived all alone in a cottage in the outskirts of a forest. He loved to see the birds and the squirrel running up and down the trees. Every morning he would throw bread crumbs and wait to see the birds and the squirrel feeding on them. One morning there was an unusual sight. The old man was not standing near his door. There weren't any bread crumbs outside either. "What's the matter?" thought the birds. "Let me peep through the window," said the squirrel and jumped on the window sill. "Grandpa, why are you still sleeping? We're waiting for you outside," whispered the squirrel. The old man jumped out of his bed and ran to open the door. And there he saw his friends. That day, the squirrel and the birds came into his house to greet him and brighten up his day.

20 Nessie's Grotto

One day a little gold fish saw a big green monster in the lake. "Who are you?" she asked nervously. "I am the Loch Ness Monster and my name is Nessie," said the fierce monster. "I've never seen you before," said the gold fish. "Nobody ever has, people only know my name," explained the monster. "How old would you be?" asked the gold fish. "Hundred and forty seven, I guess!" said the monster. "That's a lot for any animal?" reasoned the gold fish. "Well, I come from a very long line of monsters, which date back to the Prehistoric times. I believe, I am distantly related to a dinosaur called 'Mamenchisaurus'." "And what kind of food do you eat, Nessie?" asked the goldfish. "I eat fish!" explained the monster. "Fish?" asked the gold fish terrified. He promptly took a sharp turn and swam away.

21 The Aeroplane

Andy was very excited. Today, he would be sitting in an aeroplane for the first time. "When will we board the plane, Mom?" asked Andy impatiently. "Just a few minutes dear," said Mom. And then Andy saw the BIG plane! Its engine was so loud. "Vrooooomm..." On board, a pretty air hostess greeted all the passengers. She gave a candy to Andy and Andy rushed to take his seat by the window. Soon the plane was taxing down the runaway and then it soared into the sky. "We are flying," squealed Andy in delight. The trees and houses below seemed smaller and smaller as the plane went higher and higher. After a while, Andy couldn't see anything outside. There was just a white smoky fog. "Look Andy, we are in the clouds," said Mom, who was sitting beside him. "Wow!" beamed Andy. Soon, they reached their destination and the plane landed and came to a halt. Andy said 'goodbye' to the air hostess. His grandmother was waiting for him at the airport. "Grandma, I have so much to tell you..." said Andy and gave her a big hug.

22 Freddie's Cap

Once there lived two giraffes, Gertie and her baby, Freddie, in a zoo. Everyday, they would stand by their bars and people would come to have a look at them. One day, Gertie saw a group of little boys and their teacher watching and laughing at them. All the boys were wearing red caps and this really fascinated Gertie. She wished that Freddie could wear the same cap. Gertie made use of her long neck. While the teacher was telling the boys about giraffes, Gertie thrust her long neck outside the bars and pulled off a boy's cap. Pulling her neck back in, she placed the cap on Freddie's head. Seeing this, the little boy, whose cap Gertie had taken, began to cry. The zookeepers tried to get back the cap from Gertie but she would not return it. So a new cap was bought for the little boy and Freddie wore the red cap everyday.

23 Ted and His Box of Pranks

Ted loved playing pranks. One day, he took a big box to the playground. All his friends crowded around him and looked at the box curiously. "Hey, what's in that box?" asked Ralph. Ted shrugged and replied, "Oh, it's something very important. It's a secret." Sandy and John also tried their best to convince Ted to tell them what the box contained but Ted didn't reply. He sat in a corner holding his box while everyone played. Ted took his box to the playground every day and watched his friends play while he sat with the box. One evening, when all his friends were playing, Ted called them and said, "I have to run an errand. Please take care of this box for me. I'll be back soon. Remember, you must not open it." As soon as Ted left, all his friends rushed to open the mysterious box. Inside the big box was another box and inside it, there was yet another box. There were eight boxes in all, one inside the other. In the smallest box, there was a little note which said–'Too much curiosity will not get you anywhere'. Ted had played a prank on his friends again.

24 Muddy Games

Wendy's father has a big farm. Lots of cows, sheep and little white pigs live on the farm. After school, Wendy plays with all of them. Piggly Poogly piglet is his best friend. Both Wendy and his little friend love playing in the mud. There's a little muddy puddle beside the big pond in the farm. Splotch! Jump Wendy and Piggly Poogly in the puddle. The ducks and the ducklings who stay in the pond love Wendy and join in the fun. Dacky duckling loves dancing and Splitch! Splatch! He dances in the mud. Kicking the mud is one of their favourite games and everyday they hold a competition to see who kicks the mud best. Wendy always wins but what he loves best is making mud cakes. "I love the way the mud trickles down my arms and through my fingers," he says. But what Wendy dreads most is bathing. After playing in the mud, Mummy gives him a bath and scrubs him clean. Oh! What a tough time she has!

25 A Breezy Day

It's a Sunday and as usual, Mr. Walter is cleaning his garden. It's autumn and the grass is covered with dry leaves. "Come Bill, and help me clean the garden," Mr Walter shouted. Bill reluctantly agreed to help his father. Mr. Walter swept the garden and gathered the leaves into a tidy pile and Bill was just putting them into a wheelbarrow when lo! Suddenly a gust of wind blew and the leaves flew away and settled on the grass again. "Dear me!" sighed Mr. Walter, "We'll have to do it all over again." But Bill was having fun. He ran after the leaves and caught a few. The wind was so strong that the leaves were flying everywhere. "Leave them Bill," said his father. "We can sweep them some other day? How about flying a kite now?" "Hurrahhh...," cried William, "That's a great idea. It is a perfect day for flying a kite," he said and ran into the house to fetch his kite and the spool.

26 Scooby

Last week Ralph's dad got a little Scotty dog for him. "I love the Scooby Doo show so I am going to call him Scooby," said Ralph. Scooby was a very naughty dog indeed. Next day, when Granny was knitting a jumper for Scooby, he jumped on her lap and made a mess of the wool. Granny was furious but when Scooby licked Granny's face, she couldn't help smiling. In the evening, he chewed Mom's favourite slippers and he even tried to tear Ralph's books but Ralph managed to save them just in time. Scooby is getting naughtier every day. The only time when he is not creating trouble is when he is asleep. But all the same, everyone adores little Scooby and his naughty tricks.

27 The Red Truck

Roddy, a red truck, decided to take part in the 'Truck Contest' which was to take place in the neighbouring town. There was going to be a prize for the most handsome truck, the biggest truck and the smartest truck. "I think I am quite handsome," thought Roddy.

On the day of the contest, Roddy set off for the neighbouring town. It was a twenty minute drive down the hill. But alas! It had rained the night before and the roads were all muddy. As Roddy turned around a sharp bend, a truck was passing by. Splash! Some mud splattered on Roddy's windscreen. The sides were also dirty by now and the wheels were a mess. "Oh no," wailed Roddy, "I will not be able to participate in the contest now." He was almost in tears. When he reached the bottom of the hill and turned around a bend, he saw a stream of water. "Wow! Just what I need," exclaimed Roddy in delight. He stood in the stream and washed himself. Soon, he was on his way again. Amongst all the trucks, Roddy was indeed the most handsome and got a new horn for an award. It was quite a lucky day for him.

28 The Mischievous Kitten

Plum was a naughty little kitten. Mrs. Glen, her mistress, was always scolding her for her naughtiness. Mrs. Glen loved knitting. One afternoon while she was busy knitting a woollen scarf, she fell asleep. "Wow! that's a nice ball," thought Plum when she saw the woollen ball. She took the wool in her mouth and hopped around the room. Alas! Poor Plum was soon entangled in the wool and couldn't move. "Meeww..." Plum cried aloud. Mrs. Glen woke up with a jerk. "Oh, you monster...look what you've done to my wool!" she cried and quickly disentangled Plum. Then she gave her a stern look and said, "This serves you right, Kitty!" Plum was pale with fear and promised never to play with wool again.

29 Feeling Like a Champ

Arnold had been waiting impatiently for the National Reading Championship. But on the day of the final event, he was very scared. "What if I do not perform well?" thought Arnold. After all he had worked very hard and breezed through to the quarterfinals. "That was not so tough after all," thought Arnold. At the semifinals too, he performed equally well. But, the final round did not go as well as Arnold had expected. He couldn't make it to the top three. But he felt like a champion to be one of the finalists. So what if he didn't win. There's always a second time.

30 Freddy and His Little Friend

Freddy, the Labrador was annoyed when one evening his master brought home a small puppy. "Freddy boy, see I've got a young friend for you. Let's call him Pup," said his master. Freddy felt very jealous. He hung his head and walked away. Pup followed him and playfully licked Freddy. During dinner just as he was about to take his first bite, Pup slipped in between his legs and started eating from his bowl. Angry, Freddy nipped Pup hard on his hind leg. Poor Pup wept in pain. Henry quickly picked up Pup. "Bad boy, Freddy," rebuked Henry and bandaged Pup's sore leg. Freddy felt guilty and ashamed of his jealousy. He nursed Pup all night. Next morning Pup was better and Freddy gave him a big hug. "Friends?" asked Freddy. Pup smiled with delight and licked Freddy's face all over.

Contents

The Story of the Month: What a Strange House!

December

What a Strange House!

01 What a Strange House!

One morning, Vinny decided to go for a ride on her bicycle. She quickly ran upstairs and wore her shorts. "Mother, I'm going out on the bicycle," she shouted as she ran out.

"Be careful dear! Don't fall off the bicycle like you did the other day," her mother said in a worried tone. When Vinny opened the door of the shed, to her surprise, she saw that two mynas had built a nest in the bicycle's basket. Her mother who was following her saw the nest and said. "Vinny, you should not go out today. The birds will get disturbed."

Vinny was a little disappointed. "It's so strange that the birds have chosen my bicycle for a nest," she thought and decided to go for a walk. After walking for a while, she reached a cottage which was near Uncle Mike's house. She stood wondering whether she should go and meet Aunt Annie and her cousins. Just as she was about to turn to their house, Vinny was surprised to see that two swallows had built a nest in the front porch of the cottage. "That means everyone in the house will have to use the back door for a few days," thought Vinny. A little later she reached Farmer Luke's farm and saw that a duck

had laid eggs on the farmer's tractor seat! "What a sight! It seems today is a special day. I hope Farmer Luke doesn't miss those eggs on his seat. I better go and tell his wife," said Vinny, a little worried about the duck's eggs.

She walked a little further and met her friend, Julia who told her that she had found a robin's nest in a plant pot. Then the miller's wife showed her the new kittens that had made their home in a barrel. She said to Vinny, "Your grandfather has asked you to choose two kittens from here and take them home." So Vinny came home happily with the kittens that were tucked up in a basket.

When she reached home, her mother asked her, "Vinny, where are you going to keep those little kittens?"

As soon as Vinny put the basket on the floor, the kittens jumped out and ran into her dolls' house. Vinny's grandfather also came out of his room hearing the commotion.

"My my, where are those kittens you have brought?"

Everyone was surprised to see the kittens in the dolls' house, already asleep.

"What a strange house for two kittens! I'm glad I didn't go on the bicycle today," laughed Vinny. Then she told her mother all the queer houses she had seen that day.

02 A Christmas Gift

Alice did not have enough money to buy her children something for Christmas. "What shall I gift my kids this Christmas?" she thought. Suddenly she remembered that there was an old pram in the backyard that they used for collecting firewood. "I could take out the wheels and make a trolley for Misha and Glen," she thought. So, Alice got started with her work and made sure that the children were not around when she was making the trolley. On Chrismas morning, when Misha and Glen woke up, Alice said, "Children, there's something for you outside." Soon, the children were sitting in the trolley and riding down the street. In the evening, Misha and Glen hugged their mother and said, "Mother, all the children wanted a ride on our trolley. Thank you so much for the wonderful gift." Alice was very happy to hear that.

03 Jumper the Hare Gets a New Coat

Jumper Hare was worried. The snow had covered the land where he used to jump and play. "Where will I play and where will I hide?" he said to himself anxiously. In summer he had many hiding places. His brown fur was almost the same colour as the brown leaves that covered the ground, so it was difficult to spot him but now that the entire area had turned white, it had become much easier to catch sight of Jumper. One morning, Jumper woke up to find himself covered with snow. He tried to brush his coat. He brushed and brushed and brushed. To his surprise, his fur remained white and he was even more astonished the next day, when he saw that even his tail had turned white. By the next day, Jumper was all white. "At last I can hide like before," he said and danced and skipped and hopped in joy.

04 Camping out at Night

On a warm summer night Andy and his friend Jack wanted to camp out in Andy's garden. Jessie, Andy's little sister wanted to accompany them. "No, you're very small. You'll be scared at night," said Andy and Jessie started crying. Mummy rushed in and said, "Don't be so rude to her. You can take her with you." So Andy and Jack agreed to take Jessie with them. "Keep this torch with you and some chips in case you feel hungry," said Mummy and went inside the house. The children went inside the tent and zipped it from inside. They giggled and talked until they fell asleep. Wheeyeee! A strange sound woke Andy and Jack up from their sleep. But where was Jessie? They found the tent unzipped. "Bowwww!" they heard a strange voice. They screamed as a skeleton peered into the tent. Hearing the children cry, Mummy and Daddy came rushing. They found little Jessie laughing and rolling on the ground and Andy and Jack staring at her in disbelief. Jessie had put on a skeleton mask to scare the 'brave' boys.

05 The Clumsy Fairy

Susie was a very pretty fairy but she was also very clumsy. She was always dropping things around and could not sleep with her tiny wings draped around her. Every night her wings would get crushed and next morning Susie's mother had to straighten them so that she could fly properly. One day Susie flew down to the banks of the stream . She bent over to see her reflection in the clear water below. "I am so pretty," she thought and leaned further to see herself. And Oops! She toppled into the water and lost her magic wand. Susie was in tears for without a wand, she had no magical powers. A duck saw the wand flaoting in the stream and took it in the beak and flew away. Susie could not fly after the duck since her wings were heavy with water and started crying! Just then, her friend who was flying above saw Susie's plight and came to rescue her. She pulled Susie out of the water and Susie told her about the wand. She asked Susie to go to the fairy queen and ask her for a new wand. Of course, Susie got a new wand but not before she promised the fairy queen that she would never be so clumsy again.

December

06 A Fun-Filled Day

It was a nice and sunny day. Jilly and Tom were at home with Grandpa and Grandma. "Oh! It's a perfect day to be at the seaside," said Grandpa taking off his glasses. "I wish we could take the kids," said Grandma. "I am not feeling too well to handle a two hour drive to the seaside. Why don't we do something in our garden," said Grandpa. Grandpa and the kids then carried a big washing tub into the garden. Then Jilly held the hose while Grandpa turned the tap. Tom jumped into the tub and Jilly squirted water at him. "Heee! Heee!" laughed little Tom as the water tickled his ears and neck. After the tub was filled to the brim, it was time to swim. Jilly jumped into the paddling pool and Splash! Sploosh! They were splattering water everywhere. "Why don't you put some rocks and sand? suggested Grandma. So Grandpa put some small stones in the tub and sand outside and Tom brought his sailing-boat. "Oh! This is so much fun," squealed the kids and clapped their hands in delight.

07 Bobby and Alice

One day Bobby, the baby ox was walking down the street when he saw a pretty yellow calf standing and weeping by the side of the road. Bobby was very kind-hearted and so he went up to her and said, "Why are you crying? Can I help you?" "Oh thank you so much! I have lost my way and don't know where to go," sobbed the calf. Her name was Alice. Bobby felt very sorry for the poor calf and he said, "Why don't you come with me! My master is very nice. He loves me a lot and I am sure he will love you too." Alice beamed in delight and she agreed to go with Bobby. When they reached home Peter, Bobby's master was very happy to see Alice. He welcomed her warmly and she started living in his farm. Soon, Bobby and Alice became the best of friends. Every morning Alice gave a lot of milk. Peter sold the milk and very soon owned a huge farm.

08   Gabby Turns Blue

Gabby the little duckling was very naughty. One day when Mama Duck was not looking, he sneaked out of the house. He decided to go and play in the pond. On the way, he looked up at the sky and thought, "The sky is so blue. Let me try and fly in the fluffy clouds." He dived in the air, did a little jig and a somersault and happily floated in the air. "Wow…the clouds are so soft!" said he as they tickled him while he flew. Soon it was time to go back home. But Gabby couldn't find his way back home. He was lost. He flew and flew until he lost all his strength and fell down from the sky into a big cauldron containing some strange blue liquid. Now, this cauldron belonged to a magician. When Gabby finally returned home, his friends were stunned to see Gabby. His body had turned blue and his beak was white. Poor Gabby! No matter how he tried to wash himself in the pond, the colour didn't go and he is still blue.

09   Jane Goes to the City

"I am free!" mooed Jane as she ran towards the city with all her strength. She had run away from old Sam's farm after he scolded her for eating Mr. Walsh's vegetables. "Mooooo," Jane exclaimed as she reached the city. Everyone in the city seemed to be in such a hurry. And the buildings were so tall. "Skyscrapers," nodded Jane as she stared at them with wonder. Jane walked around for a while looking at everything around her. Soon, she was tired and exhausted and decided to rest for a while. She sat on the road and dozed off. Bhrmm, Bhrmm, Pom, Pom, Blrrr, Blrrr!!! The blazing sound of the horns shook Jane from her slumber. She opened her eyes and saw thousands of cars standing on the road. People were peering out of their cars and shouting at her. Jane realised that she had been sleeping in the middle of the road and was responsible for the traffic jam. Alas! She saw a police constable walking towards her. "Mooooo," she said in apology and leapt up and ran away.

December

10 Jonnie and His Pixie Friend

Little Jonnie sat at the pondside waiting for a big catch! Just then, Sarah, the little pixie in a pink dress saw Jonnie and wanted to befriend him. "Hello Jonnie, I am Sarah. Will you be my friend?" twittered the pixie flapping her tiny wings. "How did you know my name?" asked Jonnie. "We are pixies. We know everything," replied Sarah and sat beside him. Jonnie had just trapped a fish in his hook when suddenly Sarah noticed a tiny grumpy cloud above them. Then fell a drop of rain. "Oh! The rain will spoil my day," wailed Jonnie. "Don't worry. I am here. I know it's the work of naughty Nancy who loves spoiling little kids' holidays," assured Sarah and then twirling her little wand she said, "There goes my wand, whoosh and whish!" And in a wink the cloud vanished. Jonnie was very happy. "You're a nice pixie, Sarah. Will you be my friend?" said Jonnie holding out his hand.

11 The Rabbit That Didn't Grow Up

Bunny was a strange rabbit. All his friends had grown big but Bunny remained very small. He thought, "I neither fit in with the elder ones nor the younger ones. What should I do?" Just then, he saw a little girl playing with her toys. "I also want to play," said Bunny excitedly. "Go to Toy Land and become a toy first. Only then can you play with us," said a little piggy bank. "That's great!" said Bunny. He went to Toy Land where Santa Claus greeted him. Santa agreed to help Bunny. "All right, drink this potion and you will become a toy." Bunny drank it immediately and miraculously, he changed into a toy. Next Christmas, Santa secretly placed Bunny in the gift kit of a little girl called Maria. "See Mummy, what a beautiful, small bunny!" said Maria and kept it with her toys. Now, Bunny no longer thought of growing. He was happy. Maria loved Bunny and he played with her and the other toys all the time.

12 Annie in Fairyland

Annie loved fairy tales and wanted to visit Fairyland. She wished to meet Rapunzel and see Cinderella's glass slippers too! "Mummy, can I go to Fairyland?" asked Annie with wonder. "Yes Annie, you can but only in your dreams. And for that you'll have to sleep," said Mummy covering her properly. Annie fell asleep and soon she was dreaming about Fairyland. It seemed Fairyland had turned topsy-turvy. Snow White had grown her hair which almost reached her feet. Rapunzel was wearing Cinderella's glass slippers and Sleeping Beauty was playing with the seven dwarfs. And then she saw Peter Pan kissing Thumbelina on her forehead and saying, "Wake up, sweetie…" But the voice sounded so familiar. Annie opened her eyes and found Mummy leaning over her and whispering, "Wake up, sweetie. It's morning."

13 Charlie and His Tree-House

"Can we go on a jungle trip this vacation Daddy? I wanted to live in a b-i-g tree house," said Charlie. "We can have a tree house in our garden too," replied Daddy "Tree-house in our garden!" cried Charlie. "Yes dear, and I can arrange one for you," promised Daddy. So Sunday morning, Father got up early and taking his hammers, nails and tongs, climbed up a big ladder and started making a wooden house in a tree. The noise awoke Charlie and he ran into the garden and saw his father busy making a tree-house. Soon the tree-house was ready. "Hurrah!" shouted Charlie and ran inside the house to bring Mummy. "Oh, I envy you, Charlie. You have such a nice tree-house," said Mummy looking up. Charlie was very happy and thanked his Daddy. And now if you don't find him in his room, you'll know where to look for him.

14 Arnie's Caterpillar

One afternoon Arnie went outside to fly a kite. After a while, he felt something crawling on his left foot. He looked down and saw a small caterpillar trying to climb up his foot. He was just about to shake it off when he heard a faint voice calling out his name, "Arnie, Arnie." Arnie looked at the caterpillar closely and felt that the caterpillar was trying to say something to him. He knelt down and found that the caterpillar was actually trying to talk to him. The tiny caterpillar said, "I want to talk to you, Arnie. Please don't be rude to me." Arnie carefully picked up the little caterpillar and put him on his palm. "Oh, thank you, Arnie. I know you're a kind boy. I am very lonely here. All my friends have turned into beautiful butterflies and they don't even look at me now. Will you be my friend, Arnie?" said the caterpillar. Arnie felt sorry for the lonely caterpillar and agreed to be his friend. He took him inside and kept him in a glass jar in his room. Every day he takes his friend out of the jar and lets him roam around for some time.

15 Jack's Trip to Candy Mountain

Last night Jack sneaked out of his house and went to Candy Mountain! There are no rocks on Candy Mountain, there are candies instead. It's a beautiful place to be in and have fun too! It's a topsy-turvy world where people sleep by day and are awake at night. Apples grow under the ground and are as big as watermelons. And oranges are as small as strawberries. Jack saw a tree with carrots. Even cookies and chocolates grew in trees. All the children love Candy Mountain because there are no schools and no homework either! There is an orange juice spring from where orange juice gurgles down the rocks and flows down the orange juice stream. Jack loved boating here. Do you know who were with him in his boat– Dilphi Dalphi Dolphin, Pingy Pangy Penguin, some little butterflies and a sweet little Robin Redbreast. Jack knows you must be dying to meet them too. So he'll ask his friend Harry Potter to give a magic wand to each of you so that you can go with him on his next trip.

16 Rex's Centipede

One morning Rex was planting sunflowers in his garden. While digging up the soil he noticed a teeny-weeny centipede crawling out of the loose soil. Rex looked at him and thought that he was trying to tell him something. Rex took him in his palm to look at him clearly. "Rex! Rex! Don't kill me. I don't harm anybody and I am too little to be poisonous," said the tiny centipede throwing up his front legs in fright. "Why shall I kill you, dear Centipede?" asked Rex, quite surprised. "I am so sorry! I didn't know you were around. You stay here if you want. Next time I'll be careful," explained Rex. And how happy the centipede was! But as Rex put him down on the ground, the centipede tripped and shrieked. "Oh! I have lost one leg!" cried the centipede and started weeping. "Don't cry, dear Centipede. Just wait for sometime. Your leg will grow on its own," consoled Rex. "Are you sure?" asked the centipede looking up at Rex. "Yes, I am sure. I read it in my Life Science book," replied Rex. So when Rex showed him the page on Centipedes, he was happy again.

17 Norah's Diary

Last year Mummy gave Norah a beautiful blue diary and said, "Norah, look what I have got for you. It's a diary. You can share all your secrets with this diary. You can write about what you like and what you think. But remember, you must never lie to your diary." The diary was so pretty and Norah loved it. Every night before going to bed she writes in her diary. She has written about her lost pencils and how she loves to paint pictures of dolls and teddy bears. She's written about the pretty Russian doll she saw in a store the other day. Norah has been telling her diary how she plans to celebrate her birthday this year. Sometimes she draws and paints in the diary. She loves to colour the pages with her crayons. And you know, she has used all the pages already. So Mummy has given her a new diary this year. It's pink and Norah loves it just as much.

18 Shopping Fun

It was Christmas time! Little Jonnie was very excited since that day they had planned to go for shopping. "Mom! Please hurry up. We are getting late," said Jonnie to his mother while she was dressing up. "Oh dear! Don't be so impatient. I am ready," laughed Mrs. Walter while coming down the stairs. "O' Mama! You look gorgeous," exclaimed Jonnie. Freddie, his little puppy wagged his tail. "Hurrah! Off to shopping," shouted Jonnie as his Daddy started the car and Freddie wagged his tail in delight. Within fifteen minutes they reached the market. And what shopping they did! Jonnie had a new suit, new dresses, caps, shoes and so many toys. But Freddie had the best day. Mama bought him new dress, new jumper, a new hat and best of all, a nice silky ribbon to tie around his neck. Once they were back home, Jonnie tied the ribbon around Freddie's neck and put the hat on his head. "O' Freddie! You look like a gentleman," said Jonnie hugging his puppy. "Thankkuuuu!" Freddie danced on his toes.

19 Ron Learns to Get Dressed

Ron hates getting ready for school. One morning, his mother made a plan. "Wake up, Ron. It's time to play a game," said she. "Game!" wondered Ron. "If you want to play this game you must hurry," said Mummy. Ron was very excited and quickly washed his face and had his bath. "I have hidden your clothes in your room. I am going to count one to thirty and you'll have to find them and put them on. So are you ready?" explained Mummy 'Yes, I am," said Ron as he dashed to his room. As Mummy started counting, "One…two…" Ron searched the whole room. He found his hat and one sock on his toy train. Then he got his pants from under the pillow and his shirt was hanging on the clock. He quickly put these on. But where is the other sock? Ron searched for a while and finally found it under the cupboard! "And thirty!" said Mummy. Just then Ron announced, "I am ready!" So Ron finally learnt to dress up alone!

20 Old Peter's Turnip

Old Peter had planted some turnip plants in his garden. One day he saw that one of them had grown really b-i-g! "Aha! That's quite like a giant for a turnip. What a pleasure! I can have plenty of turnip soup now," he said. So Peter cheerfully started pulling it up. But lo! The turnip proved to be stronger than him and he landed on the ground after doing a somersault. Quite miffed at this, he called his wife for help. Mrs. Peter was a short, rotund lady. She held Peter from behind and together they started pulling the turnip, but alas! They both tumbled to the ground. Just then, Mr. Walker, their neighbour was passing by their house and decided to help them. But the three of them couldn't move the turnip either. So Mr. Walker called Jacky, his dog. Jacky held Mr. Walker's trousers and they tried to pull the turnip out but the turnip refused to budge. A cat also pitched in to help but they still couldn't move the turnip. Finally the cat called over Randy rat and the six of them pulled and pulled and finally the turnip was out.

21 Ronald and the Bumblebee

Ronald's father had a farm house and Ronald loves spending time with the animals there. His friends were Alice the cow, Randy the horse and Bobby the little white pig. One day, Ronald noticed a big beehive and called out, "Is anyone there?" Now, the beehive belonged to hundreds of bees. All the bees had gone out. The queen bee, who usually stays back wasn't in the hive either. There was just a small bumblebee who wasn't feeling well and had stayed back. So when bumblebee heard Ronald's voice he was very excited. He came out from the hive and buzzed, "Hey, I am Buzz. Who are you?" Soon Ronald and the bumblebee became good friends. Buzz was crazy about honey. One day Ronald was eating honey and smeared it all over his clothes and hair. Oh, it was such a mess! It was Buzz's happiest day. He buzzed around Ronald all day until Ronald decided to have a bath and scrub himself clean.

22 Presence of Mind

Gerald lived with his mother and his little sister in a small hut near a railway track. Everyday when his mother would go to fetch vegetables from the market in the evening, Gerald would sit by the window and watch the trains passing by. One day when Gerald was baby sitting his sister and trying his best to put her to sleep, he looked out of the window and saw that there was a crack in the track. He could hear a train approaching. "I need to stop the train somehow," thought Gerald and rushed out. The train was approaching at a great speed. Gerald didn't know what to do. Just then he had an idea. He took his shirt off and started waving it in the air frantically. The train driver saw him and sensed that something was wrong. He stopped the train immediately. Everyone praised Gerald for preventing an accident and saving many lives.

23 Harry and Mr. Bunny

One day little Harry was walking across the frozen hills. He was going to see whether the snowman he made the day before still stood there. "Oh, my snowman is still there!" exclaimed Harry as he saw the snowman from a distance and cheerfully hurried his pace. As he reached near it he found a little bunny staring at the snowman with wonder. "Hello! Mr. Bunny, why are you staring at it?" asked little Harry leaning down. The bunny looked up to Harry and said, "Hello!" Then he continued, "See, I am talking to this man but he is not responding. Neither he is moving nor is he twinkling his eyes. It's so strange! And see he is so white unlike you!" "Ha! Ha! Ha!" Harry broke into laughter, "Dear Bunny, he is not a real man. He is a snowman. Yesterday I made him with the snow that is lying under our feet. That's why he doesn't move, doesn't talk and never blinks his eyes." "Oh, you made it!" exclaimed the little bunny clasping his little paws in wonder. "This is s-o-o-o nice. Can you make a snow-bunny just like me?" the bunny continued. Harry was delighted. "Why not dear Bunny! You just stand here while I make a snow bunny just like you," replied Harry cheerfully taking a lump of snow in his hand.

24 The Snow-Girl

Old Arthur and his wife were two kind souls. They were a cheerful couple always helping others with this or that. "Look how happy Old Arthur and his wife are," their neighbours would often say. But Old Arthur and his wife were not so happy in their hearts because they didn't have any children. One day the couple went for a stroll on the snowy ground near their house. Mrs. Arthur picked up some snow and made a pretty snowgirl. "How I wish I had a lovely daughter like this," said Mrs. Arthur looking at the snowgirl wistfully and tears rolled down her cheeks. Now, Santa Claus was checking all the wish lists that he got from the children round the world. He heard Mrs. Arthur crying and felt very sorry for her. Then suddenly he had a bright idea. Meanwhile, Arthur and his wife were about to turn back to return home when suddenly the snowgirl blinked her eyes and before the old couple knew what was happening, a strong wind blew and blinded their eyes. When they opened their eyes they saw a pretty girl standing in front of them. "I am your daughter," said the girl smiling sweetly. Arthur and his wife were delighted. Suddenly they saw a paper pinned on the girl's dress. On it was written, "To two wonderful people."

25 Mr. Jonathan's Cat

Mr. Jonathan had a little cat who was very naughty. She used to eat all the fish, lazed on the sofa and never bothered to catch any mice. Mr. Jonathan was tired of her. So he wrapped her in a rug and asked a little boy to take the little bundle and leave it somewhere far. The boy took the cat to a deserted place and left the rug untied. Next morning when Mr. Jonathan woke up, he saw the cat curled up beside him. He put the cat in a box and arranged to have it put in as train. A few days later when Mr. Jonathan went to the kitchen, he saw his cat was busy eating fish again! Frustrated, Mr. Jonathan put her on board a ship getting ready to sail. The ship hit a storm in the mid-ocean and Mr. Jonathan thought that was the last he would hear of his cat. But surprisingly, the cat came back after a few days and Mr. Jonathan never ever tried to send her away again.

26 Why the Sky is so High

"Mummy, why is the sky so high? It would have been so nice if we could raise our hand and touch it," said little Terry one day, after Mummy tucked him to bed at night. "Oh, that's a very old story, Terry. I can tell you if you promise that you'll sleep after I finish." "Yes, Yes, of course I will," promised Terry, all eager to hear another exciting story. "A long time ago, the sky was very low. People could touch the sky and talk to the clouds. The Sun was very hot so nobody went near it. At that time an old woman used to live near the horizon where the sky was very low indeed. This woman lived alone and spent the whole day cleaning her house. One year the summer was especially hot and the land was very dry. There was dust everywhere. The old woman didn't like this so she decided to sweep the dust away. But the more she swept the dusty pathway, the more dust rose around her in large volumes and she almost choked. Poor Sky! The dust got into his eyes, nose and everywhere and he coughed and sneezed till water came out of his eyes in large drops. His tears dropped on the ground and made the dusty ground muddy. The woman got very angry. 'Why have you made it sloppy,' she screamed at the sky and before he could explain she started smacking him hard with her broom. The sky had to run away higher up to save himself and since then he stays up there. So that's the end of the story, Terry. Now be a good boy and go to sleep," said Mummy putting off the light.

27 Mr. Wilson and Bobby Bear

Mr. Wilson has a small grizzly bear for a pet. His name is Bobby. If you pass by Mr. Wilson's house on Sundays or on a holiday you'll catch them flying kites. Bobby is quite good at flying kites. Or otherwise, Mr. Wilson takes him to the seaside and they enjoy themselves. They play football, they swim, they make sand castles…they do whatever they feel like. But if they want to have a candy or ice creams they find no candy man or ice cream vendor or for that matter anybody on the beach. Do you know why? That's because when Mr. Wilson takes Bobby bear with him, everybody on the beach runs away in fright and Mr. Wilson and Bobby have the entire beach to themselves. But in winters you can't find Bobby anywhere because he curls up and hibernates in his cave which he has made for himself in a corner of Mr. Wilson's garden. When winter is over, he comes out of his cave. After sleeping for so long Bobby feels very hungry and growls for food. And if you give him a big jar of honey, he is happy and ready to play again.

28 Mr. Toby Regains His Life

Mr. Toby was a very handsome and rich cat. After all, he was Mrs. Wilson's pet. He was reading a letter which was from Miss Chloe, the most beautiful cat. "Toby! My heart aches for you. I am dying for your love. Will you marry me?" Chloe had written. Toby couldn't believe his eyes. He received many love letters now and then. But to know that Chloe was madly in love with him was quite a piece of good news. He got up and began dancing on the wooden roof in excitement. He hopped and jumped so happily that quite expectedly he tripped and fell off the roof and died. The entire cat community joined the funeral procession with a sobbing Mrs. Wilson and an unconsolable Miss Chloe following them. As the procession passed the market square, the smell of fish was very strong. It stirred Mr. Toby from his death-sleep. "M-e-o-w," yawned Toby and opened his eyes. And "MEOW" cheered all happily.

29 The Swan Girl

Once upon a time there lived a poor weaver and his wife in a small cottage. One wintry night they heard a knock at their door. When they opened the door they were surprised to find a beautiful girl dressed in a white silvery robe shivering in the cold. The old couple quickly brought her in and asked her to stay with them. One day the girl said, "Father, I'll weave a stole for you every night. But you must promise that while I am weaving, no one will come into my room." Though surprised, the old man agreed and that night the girl shut herself in a room. Early morning, she came out with a rich and beautiful silvery stole. The old couple was stunned to see the beautiful stole! This went on for a few days until one night curiosity overcame them and they peeped into their daughter's room. And lo! There was a beautiful silver swan weaving with her silver feathers. The swan saw them and said in a sad voice, "Now that you have seen me, I can't stay here anymore though I would have loved to stay here forever." Saying so, she flew away.

30 The Hunchback and the Fairies

One day a hunchback went to a forest to cut wood. Soon, it became dark and so he decided to spend the night in the forest. At night, he woke up and heard someone singing very melodiously. Enchanted by the voice, he decided to follow the direction of the sound. He soon reached a place where a group of fairies were singing and dancing around a fire: "Ring-a-ring-a around the fire. Let's sing and dance to the song of the lyre." The man, however, noticed that they were singing these two lines repeatedly. He walked up to them and said, "Don't be angry, dear fairies. I heard your beautiful voice and came here. But you are just singing two lines. I can teach you many songs which my mother sang to me when I was a child. Do you want to hear them?" The fairies nodded and the man started singing some beautiful songs. The fairies were filled with joy. Noticing the hunch, they asked him to kneel and then touched his back with their magic wands. And lo! The hunch disappeared making the man fit and strong.

31 Grandma Brings Malcolm Back

Martha and Marc had a naughty little dog called Malcolm. He was always up to mischief. He would disappear with the newspaper, chew grandma's slippers or eat all the cookies. He was quite a bundle of trouble. Grandma was always complaining, "Why doesn't he learn how to behave?" she often complained.

But no matter how much Martha or Marc scolded Malcolm, he only wagged his tail happily.

One day Malcolm disappeared. He couldn't be found anywhere. Martha and Marc were heartbroken. Everyone was in tears except Grandma who didn't seem to be affected by Malcolm's absence. "Everything is in order now, so clean and tidy," said Grandma.

After a few days, when Martha and Marc were in their study, they heard Grandma shouting for them. They rushed out to see Grandma holding Malcolm in her arms. "Malcolm!" shrieked the children in delight. Grandma explained that she saw him being taken away in a police van and followed the van to bring him back. The police had thought that he had gone astray. "But Grandma, you don't even like Malcolm," said Marc. "Well," said Grandma, "I missed him so much when he went away. I am so glad that he is back now." Martha and Marc hugged Grandma and beamed with joy.